Local Area Networks

A User's Guide for Business Professionals

James Harry Green

SCOTT, FORESMAN and COMPANY
Glenview, Illinois   London

Library of Congress Cataloging in Publication Data

Green, James H. (James Harry)
  Local area networks.

  Bibliography: p.
  Includes index.
  1. Local area networks (Computer networks) I. Title.
TK5105.7.G74   1985   384   84–14062

ISBN 0-673-18065-4

1 2 3 4 5 6-RRC-89 88 87 86 85 84

LIST OF TRADEMARKS

ALSPA-NET is a trademark of Alspa Computer, Inc.
ARCNET is a trademark of Datapoint Corporation.
AXIS is a trademark of Ztel.
Cinchnet is a trademark of Iconix Corporation.
Cluster One is a trademark of Nestar Corp.
C-Net is a trademark of Cromemco.
CompuStar is a trademark of Intertec Data Systems.
ContelNet and STAR-Eleven are trademarks of Contel Information
    Systems.
DBS-Net is a trademark of DBS International.
DCS-2/25 Data Carrier is a trademark of Teltone Corporation.
DECdataway is a trademark of Digital Equipment Corporation.
Decision Net and MIRLAN are trademarks of NCR Corporation.
Develnet is a trademark of Develeon Electronics, Inc.
DLX-10 and DLX-320 are trademarks of Computer Network.
Doeltz is a trademark of Doeltz Network, Inc.
ELAN is a trademark of Braegen Corporation.
Ethernet and Xerox are trademarks of Xerox Corporation.
Etherseries, EtherShare, Ethermail, Ethernet/UNET, and Etherlink are
    trademarks of 3COM Corporation.
Fiber Optic Net/One, Net/One Baseband, Net/One Broadband, and
    Net/One Thin Coax are trademarks of Ungermann-Bass, Inc.
FiberLAN and Fiber Wiring Center are trademarks of Siecor Corporation.
GEnet is a trademark of General Electric.
G/Net is a trademark of Gateway Communications, Inc.
HiNet is a trademark of Digital Microsystems, Inc.
HYPERchannel and HYPERbus are trademarks of Network Systems
    Corporation.
IBM is a trademark of International Business Machines Corporation.
IBX, InteNet, and LANmark are trademarks of the Intecom Corporation.
IDX-3000 is a trademark of M/A-COM Linkabit, Inc.
INSTANET is a trademark of Micom Systems.
Interface Bus, LAN 9000, and SRM are trademarks of Hewlett-Packard.
LAN/1 and VIDEODATA are trademarks of Interactive Systems/3M.
LANmark is a trademark of Intecom, Inc.
LBS 5000 is a trademark of Lanier.
LINC is a trademark of Vector Graphics.
Local Resource = Sharing Network is a trademark of Convergent
    Technologies.
LocalNet 20 and LocalNet 40 are trademarks of Sytek, Inc.
Lotus 123 and Lotus are trademarks of Lotus Development Corporation.
Messenger is a trademark of Amtel Systems.
MIC-LINK is a trademark of Sidereal Corporation.
Millway is a trademark of Valmet, Inc.
MODBUS and MODWAY are trademarks of Gauld, Inc.
MORROW NETWORK is a tradename of Morrow.
Multibus is a trademark of Intel Corporation.
Multilink is a trademark of Davong Systems, Inc.
Multiplan is a trademark of Microsoft Corporation.
NBINET is a trademark of NBI, Inc.

Net/One is a trademark of Codex Corporation.
NET/PLUS is a trademark of Interlan Corp.
NorthNet is a trademark of North Star Computer.
Nova, Eclipse, XODIAC Network Bus, and MV Series are trademarks of Data General Corporation.
OmegaNET is a trademark of Compucorp.
Omninet is a trademark of Corvus, Inc.
PACXNET is a trademark of Gandalf Data Inc.
PC Cluster and Series/1 Ring are trademarks of International Business Machines (IBM).
PCnet and PCnet/Plus are trademarks of Orchid Technology, Inc.
PercomNet is a trademark of Percom Data Corporation.
PLAN 4000 Series is a trademark of Nestar Systems.
PLANET is a trademark of Racal-Milgo.
Polynet is a trademark of Logica, Inc.
Proloop is a trademark of Prolink Corporation.
proNet is a trademark of Proteon Associates, Inc.
RINGNET is a trademark of Prime Computer, Inc.
ROLM, Cypress, ROLMphone, ROLMbus, and CBXII, are trademarks of ROLM Corporation.
SDSNET is a trademark of Scientific Data.
ShareNet is a trademark of Novell Data Systems.
SHINPADS is a trademark of Sperry.
STAR-Eleven is a trademark of Contel Information Systems.
Starnet II is a trademark of Starnet Data Systems.
StrataLINK is a trademark of Stratus Computer, Inc.
SuperMicro multiuser is a trademark of Molecular Company.
SYNNet is a trademark of Syntrex, Inc.
TDC 3000 is a trademark of Honeywell.
Telenet is a trademark of General Telephone and Electonics.
Teletype is a trademark of AT&T Teletype.
The Loop is a trademark of A.B. Dick Company.
TIENET is a trademark of Pragmatronics.
Token/Net is a trademark of Concord Data Systems.
Tymnet is a trademark of Tymnet, Inc.
ULCnet is a trademark of Orange Compuco, Inc.
ULTRANET is a trademark of Inforex, Inc.
UNET is a trademark of Zilog, Inc.
UniLAN is a trademark of Appletek Corporation.
VAX and PDP-11 are trademarks of Digital Equipment Corporation.
VisiCalc is a trademark of Visocorp Corporation.
WangNet and Wang Band are trademarks of Wang Laboratories, Inc.
WorkNet is a trademark of Altos Computer Systems.
XLAN is a trademark of Complexx Systems, Inc.
XYPLEX is a trademark of Xyplex, Inc.

Preface

The remainder of the 1980s will see an explosion in the growth of computer networks. The computer has reached its maturity as a data procesing tool. However, while on the verge of the information age, the computer's potential as an information processor has hardly been tapped.

The information age has been described by such observers as Toffler and Naisbitt as the era in which our economy is shifting from the production of goods to that of information. The idea of information as a commodity is a bit hard to get used to. As consumers most of our money goes for goods, and the services we buy have only a small information content. Typically, the largest consumers of information have been business and governments, but increasingly, private individuals are interested in information and are willing to pay for it.

Individual consumers survive well with infrequent excursions to information sellers such as lawyers, accountants, engineers, or architects, but information is the lifeblood of businesses and government. Financial, administrative, production, and economic decisions are based on information stored in data bases and computer files shared by many organization decision makers. The growing trend toward distributed processing and the increasing use of desktop computers and terminals to access data bases are driving the development of a new breed of data network systems—the local area network.

Data networks are nothing new. In their earliest form, data files were sent over telegraph wires. Human beings converted information from the written form to electrical impulses and back to the written form at the remote end. Around the turn of the century, the teletypewriter began to displace the telegrapher, and by the second half of this decade mechanization had reached maturity. Now humans intervene only to keyboard the information initially. And even that is changing as computers create information and other forms of data entry such as optical character reading and computer voice recognition begin to develop.

One significant change just emerging is the development of private local networks. Private networks existed in the past, but they were usually implemented over common carrier facilities. However, the Bell System split-up and the rapid growth of other carriers have made many options available to private users. Moreover, common carrier networks are costly for short-range communications. Studies show that a substantial portion—perhaps as much as 80 percent—of data communications is transmitted over a limited area; an office, a building, or a campus. The amount of long-range communication varies with the organization, but many offices can get by with little data communication outside their own bounds.

Although the cost of computers and terminals is declining, the cost of peripheral equipment such as disk drives and high-speed printers has not dropped proportionately. Moreover, the cost of program development keeps some applications centralized; this generates the need for remote-terminal communications with central computers requiring specialized software and high-speed disk drives. As the day approaches for putting a terminal on nearly every desk, there is a growing need to share these costly devices that are accessed only occasionally.

Furthermore, data communications is becoming an important part of every office automation system. In some applications, such as electronic mail, communications is the essence of the application. While the cost of computers declines, the cost of communications has kept some applications centralized that would otherwise be more economical if distributed. Another problem that has plagued terminal users is the difficulty of interfacing dissimilar devices because they have been designed even up to now with so little compatibility.

These trends—the growth in data communications, availability of affordable terminals and storage, sharing of high cost peripherals, incompatibility of communication devices, and an explosion in organizational information needs—have led to the development of specialized networks designed for high-speed economical communication over short distances. These networks are called "local area networks" or simply "local networks." In this book we will generally use the latter term to include both local area networks, which are multiple access local networks connected over cable, and circuit switched networks connected through data switches and private branch exchanges (PBXs).

With any new set of products, the user is bombarded with a great deal of confusing terminology, conflicting claims, and sometimes plain hype. Such has been the case with local networks. Extravagant claims have been made for the advantages of broadband over baseband and vice versa, multiple access over the PBX, fiber optics over coaxial cable—every application has its advocates and its critics. Moreover, except for older generations of PBX, current local networks have not been widely applied, making it difficult to rely on the experiences of others in deciding what claims to accept.

With the advent of the automated office, the use of local networks is about to take a gigantic leap forward. In the course of applying office automation, many organizations will be evaluating the kind of local network they need, but most users are not concerned with the technology of the local network any more than they are about how the telephone network functions. All they want to know is that it does work, and how to use it. The main purpose of the local network is to increase the value of information by improving its accessibility and increasing the speed of distribution. The less users have to know about the technology the better.

This book is addressed to users and to those who select office automation and other applications of local networks such as computer aided design and manufacturing. The book is written with a particular point of view—there is no such thing as a universal solution to the local network problem. Each of the new technologies has its range of applications. The appropriate technology to apply is the one that best matches your application. The purpose of this book, therefore, is to help you to understand your application, to be aware of the strengths and weaknesses of local network options available on the market, and, ultimately, to decide which option to apply.

Wherever it is appropriate, we provide brief descriptions of commercially available local networks to illustrate the techniques used in practice. These descriptions contain enough information to give you an overview of the product, but they are not complete surveys. Furthermore, products are changing so rapidly that there is no assurance that these examples represent the latest version. These descriptions should not be relied on as anything more than a vehicle to help understand the widely diverging techniques on the market today.

This book has an additional message. It is tempting to delay acquiring a network: the technology changes so fast that it is difficult to keep up with the changes, and undoubtedly there will be improvements in the future. However, delaying is a poor strategy for most organizations that need a network now. By using available technology, you will prepare yourself to absorb future advances as they occur. The goal should be to learn how to increase the usefulness of information in the office. Local networks and automation can aid in solving business problems by providing the means for making information accessible and usable by formatting it intelligently and distributing it widely within the organization.

Contents

1

Rationale of the Local Network

In this era of instantaneous communication, with emphasis on global picture and voice transmissions over satellite circuits, we must remind ourselves that about 80 percent of a typical organization's communication takes place within a narrow radius. People and the machines that support them exchange most information within the bounds of a building, an office complex, or a campus. At present much of this exchange is in the form of telephone conversations and the office mail, but with rising salaries and the need to use the power of computers to improve productivity, communication between data terminals and computers will comprise an ever increasing share of total communication in an organization.

Communication between office machines is nothing new. It began with the invention of the teletypewriter in 1904, but today's office machines bear as much resemblance to the teletypewriter as a Boeing 767 does to Phineas Fogg's balloon. Teletypewriters were developed for transmitting documents over long distances. With the automated office, today's machines can provide economical communication between people within earshot of one another. This narrowing of the economical communication distance results from the use of modern data terminal equipment not only to communicate,

1

but also to support the productivity of the office worker in handling text and data.

With the changing milieu of the office comes a change in the way office machines communicate. When the distances were vast, machines were either interconnected with a fixed or "point-to-point circuit" or switched together by a central operator or switching machine. But it is not economical to wire a circuit halfway across town merely to connect to the person at the next desk if a reasonable alternative exists. The trend toward the automated office and distributed data processing demands a network specially designed for swift and easy communication within a single organizational entity. In the jargon of the industry, such a network is known as a **local network** or **local area network,** often referred to as **LAN.**

WHAT IS A LOCAL NETWORK?

In the current vernacular the two terms local network and local area network are often used interchangeably. There is no universally accepted distinction between the two, but in this book we shall use local network as a more inclusive term, encompassing both local area networks and circuit-switching systems such as **private branch exchanges** (PBXs) and specialized data switches. A LAN is usually characterized as a network dedicated to a single organization, limited in the distance it serves, and interconnected by some common communication technology.

This definition has some important implications. Because the network is private, it can be specialized for the function it is intended to perform. Security may not be as important as it is in multi-user networks. Because it is limited in distance, a local network can operate at high speeds. Private circuit switches meet all the above distinctions except for the last. Typically, circuit switches transport data at a slower rate than a LAN, although with changes in technology, this distinction is fading.

Local networks can also be defined in contrast with their counterparts, metropolitan and global networks. The main distinctions between the three are the distance serviced, the data speed, and the routing complexity. Transmission costs over networks are a function of speed or bandwidth, and distance. Although satellite circuits and packet-switched data networks are erasing some of the relationships between cost and distance, in general, the longer the serviced distance, the higher the cost for a given speed. Therefore, global networks tend to cover lower speeds and longer distances than metropolitan networks and local networks.

With circuit switching, routing is implicit in the network because data is transported over a circuit confined to a pair of users. In most LANs, data is accessible to all users, so addressing takes the place of routing. Metropolitan and global networks connect to other networks through gateway circuits or tandem switching machines. Processors are used to route by routing tables and to translate between the communication protocols of other networks.

No two users of data communication have identical requirements. Each type of network has advantages over the others, and each has different design objectives. There is little agreement among the vendors on how to implement or interconnect local networks; however, the demand will grow to the point that buildings will be wired for a network as routinely as they are now wired for telephone and electric service.

WHY AN ORGANIZATION NEEDS A LOCAL NETWORK

From its infancy to its maturity, data processing involved a central computer directly wired to peripheral devices such as tape drives, printers, and disk drives. Computers were employed to communicate with distant terminals, but such communication was often incidental to the primary need to batch-process a great deal of data centrally and by the most economical means. Batch data processing still exists and will continue to grow as long as the computer retains its grip on the organization, but text processing is becoming equally important.

SHARING COMMON DATA BASES

With Intel's development of the microprocessor in 1970, the nature of data processing began to evolve in a way that is still imperfectly understood; it will be subject to a great deal more development. The microprocessor made it possible for processing power to be distributed to a multitude of remote devices. The computer-on-a-chip is now so inexpensive that it replaces wired logic in electronic devices from microwave ovens to automobile ignitions. Because of this inexpensive processing power, in the future we will see a merger of text and data processing systems. They will share common data bases, common terminals, and a common need to communicate rapidly with each other. This trend will grow because of the difficulty of managing information with multiple data bases and the currently low level of integration of office functions.

INFORMATION ACCESSIBILITY

In the future, systems will aid people in communicating with words, numbers, images, and speech, all of which are defined collectively as information. Information flows in diverse directions, and to be effective, people must deal with it more or less simultaneously. The old methods of handling information on paper will give way to the terminals of the new information age. A major purpose of the local network is to promote the value of information by increasing its speed of distribution and its accessibility.

For example, in most modern offices people frequently change their work locations. The cost of wiring terminals becomes a significant portion of the total cost of the move, not to mention the time delays and lost productivity. The problem of moving terminals can be solved with a properly designed local network, which by its very nature is not affected by the physical location of a terminal. When information is broadcast, the addressee needs only to recognize and detect messages addressed to it.

INCREASING USE OF TERMINALS

In the United States over half the more than 100 million employed persons are in white-collar occupations. Relative to changes in agriculture and manufacturing changes, office jobs have hardly been touched by mechanization. Except for word processor operators, most office workers rarely encounter a device more complicated than an electric typewriter. However, if we are to believe the pundits of the automated office, that is about to change. By the end of the decade, the video display terminal on the office desk should be nearly as common a device as the telephone. In fact, there is a great deal of evidence that the two may be integrated.

Besides their application in the automated office, terminals are rapidly gaining use in distributed data processing. Such functions as remote order entry, inventory control, and the countless electronic cash registers and point-of-sale terminals are cases in point. But the automated office is more than the mere application of distributed data processing. Office workers process information in verbal, textual, and numerical form; and the distinction among them is important.

Information is not static. It flows dynamically through the office, and any systems that impede it are detrimental to productivity. The essence of the automated office and of distributed processing is the ability of people to use machines to access one another instantaneously with a direct, economical connection. This access should be accomplished through familiar languages and simple protocols. This is the function of local networks in their variety of forms and styles.

CHANGING NATURE OF OFFICE COMMUNICATION

Communication has become a part of virtually every computing system, and in some areas such as electronic mail, it is the application. While the declining price of computers has resulted in increases both in their capacity and number, other costs have remained high. The costs of communications, program development, and peripherals such as high-speed printers and high-capacity disk drives have made it more economical to leave many applications centralized when it would be more efficient to distribute them. Of course, it is not necessarily desirable to distribute all data processing applications, but there is definitely a need for an inexpensive, high-speed network to allow many small computers and terminals to share common information resources.

LIMITATIONS OF CONVENTIONAL NETWORKS

Throughout the years, most data communications have taken place over conventional telephone facilities on either a switched or point-to-point basis. These facilities were designed for voice traffic and fit that purpose admirably. Voice communication over a network starts with dialing a connection. Dialing takes about five seconds, and the communication typically lasts for four or five minutes. As a percentage of the total connection time, the dialing time is insignificant. With the advent of tone dialing, some improvement has been made. It now takes no longer to dial a zero than a one, and push buttons are more convenient than a rotary dial, but the improvement is more a convenience than a true gain in productivity.

TIME REQUIRED FOR CONNECTIONS

With data terminals, the dialing time can be a significant drawback. In the five seconds that it takes to set up a call, a data terminal can transmit an entire message at ordinary speeds, release the circuit, and be ready for another call. The nature of machine communications demands an entirely different concept for establishing and processing machine-to-machine connections.

BURSTY NATURE OF DATA TRAFFIC

In contrast to voice communication, which is protracted, data communication is often bursty. To be sure, remote data entry terminals and batch printers can be connected for hours to a computer for processing a single job, but that is not the nature of the automated office. Its multi-function environment can include electronic mail, electronic filing and retrieval, and personal support systems such as the automated in-basket—applications that require only a few seconds of connection time. Moreover, traditional telephone circuits are too expensive to dedicate to data terminals, for by design, their narrow bandwidth restricts the speed or throughput of terminal-to-terminal connections. The automated office requires a network to overcome these limitations.

NEED TO ADDRESS MULTIPLE RESOURCES

In a computer network, users need to address multiple resources on the network quickly and easily. For example, a disk, a tape, a terminal, a gateway—any of these resources can be addressed symbolically. Moreover, the user isn't interested in how the network functions. Outside of security procedures, users need unrestricted access to geographically dispersed resources.

ISSUES CONFRONTING THE LAN USER

While the entire industry concurs with the need for a local network, there is little unanimity about the form it should take. In this book, we will discuss the issues in depth. We will not conclude that there is a single ideal form of the local network because, despite the claims of the vendors, no single ideal local network exists. An insurance company occupying a single floor of a Manhattan office building has different requirements than the multiple departments of a university; yet both are potential users of a local network.

In this book we will explore the issues with this objective in mind: to provide you with enough understanding of the issues so that you will be able to choose from the many alternatives on the market those best suited to your needs.

STANDARDS AND COMPATIBILITY

If there has been one pervasive problem in the short history of data communications, it has been lack of compatibility. For the first fifty years of machine communication, compatibility was a minor problem because most machines communicated in baudot, a simple code named after its French inventor, J. M. E. Baudot. Machines communicated in a combination of marks and spaces analogous to the dots and dashes of international Morse code and to the zeros and ones data processing machines use today. Until about 1960, the Baudot code, converted to audible tones, was in widespread commercial use over long distance telephone circuits. In local telephone circuits, the tones were converted to current pulses that traveled over local wire facilities to the terminal machine.

With the invention of the computer and the explosive growth of data communications, the coding scheme and the transmission method were no longer adequate. Unfortunately, they were not replaced with a universal standard. Instead, multiple languages developed, causing an impediment to open communications.

The problems extend beyond the code, however. Machines speak different languages and use different conventions—**protocols** in data communications terminology. These problems are compensated for by a process akin to that used in the United Nations where translators must rebroadcast information to the delegates' headsets.

Most organizations will not evolve into an automated office through a sudden conversion. On the contrary, the conversion will be gradual; an important economic and productivity factor will be the question of obsolescence for existing machines as the office evolves toward automation. One major function of the local network, therefore, is to ensure the compatibility of a wide variety of data terminals, translating as necessary, and ensuring that all communicate with common conventions.

Several national and international organizations have attempted to introduce standards into local networks, but none has been universally accepted and exceptions to the standards will likely exist for many years. It is important, therefore, to understand the nature of these standards. To deviate from them requires full understanding of the consequences. Chapter 4 is devoted to a discussion of local network standards and the agencies that set them.

COMPATIBILITY WITH OTHER NETWORKS

Rarely is a local network able to function entirely within its own bounds. Somehow it must interface with other networks, often on a world-wide basis. As global networks have been in existence for many years, they have rigidly defined protocols that are designed for purposes beyond local network needs. Therefore, the local network must adapt to the external network protocols to give it the flexibility of handling traffic outside its narrow bounds.

SPEED

The speed of transmission is an important distinction between local networks. Most circuit switches pass data at a lower rate than true local area networks. Older PBXs are limited by the speeds of their switching networks or their line interface circuits, and are therefore much slower than newer **computerized branch exchanges** (CBXs).

The speed of transmission in a network can be misleading. Manufacturers typically state the data transfer rate of the LAN. For example, Ethernet has a data speed of 10 mb/s. The actual **throughput** of the network, however, will be less—3 mb/s is typical, depending on the data load, the protocol, and numerous other factors. As we discuss the various means of implementing local networks, we will address the factors limiting speed and how they affect the throughput rate.

ACCESS METHOD

Data communication devices generally access one another by one of three methods: they are wired on dedicated point-to-point circuits, they are switched together, or multiple devices share the transmission time of a single high-speed circuit. When a data terminal is connected to a network, it must have a means for signaling its intention to send data, it must be capable of being addressed with compatible data, and it must interfere to the least degree possible with other devices. Networks use switching, multiple access, polling, and direct or dedicated wiring for the terminals and computers to gain access to one another.

In the strictest sense of the word, these methods are not all applicable to the local network; but in our definition of interconnecting data devices for a single organization within a narrow geographical range, they all apply. The free interconnection of all office automation devices is an important issue we must deal with in acquiring a satisfactory local network. This issue is so vital that we will devote a chapter to discussing each access method.

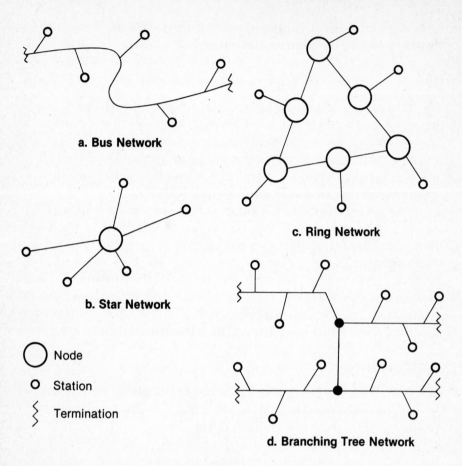

a. Bus Network

b. Star Network

c. Ring Network

d. Branching Tree Network

Node

Station

Termination

FIGURE 1.1   Network topologies

TRANSMISSION MEDIUM

In the past, the choice of transmission medium was simple; paired copper wire was used almost exclusively for short distances, with long haul circuits implemented over coaxial cable, radio, or voice carrier. Recently, coaxial cable, or "coax," has become an important local network transmission medium. Coax has a wide bandwidth. Telephone companies have used it since the 1940s for long haul voice circuits. More recently, cable television technology married data communications to enable sharing by time and frequency division multiplexing.

With **time division multiplexing** (TDM), each terminal is connected to the coax for an instant, giving it an effective full-time connection to the receiving terminal. With **frequency division multiplexing** (FDM), the bandwidth of the transmission medium is divided into multiple channels with each channel assigned to a particular frequency. TDM and FDM are important local network concepts that will be explained more fully in Chapter 5.

A more recent development with significant networking potential is fiber optics. By sending light pulses over glass pipes finer than a human hair, an unbelievable amount of data can be transmitted. Current technology enables transmission of 540 million bits per second (mb/s) between terminals. To put its capacity in perspective, at 540 mb/s, the 43,000,000 words in the Encyclopedia Brittanica could be transmitted in about four seconds.

TOPOLOGY

The pattern of interconnecting terminals on a network is the network's architecture or topology. Figure 1.1 illustrates the most common topologies of the network, which are discussed in Chapter 2. Topology is closely related to the access method and transmission medium and is normally chosen as a function of the design of the network. For example, contention networks normally use a bus topology and coaxial or fiber optic cable.

SUMMARY

This discussion should make evident the many issues confronting the user of local networks. Throughout this volume, we endeavor to decode the language of local network designers and vendors. We use terminology that people with limited data communication knowledge can understand and apply.

This book is application oriented. It is directed to the potential user of a local network, or to someone who wants a comfortable understanding of the technology without getting immersed in the details. Where explanations are needed to make the technical meaning clear, we will pause long enough to provide them. The reader who already understands the technical aspects can skip those explanations.

Network Alternatives

2

Communication networks all share a common objective: to interconnect terminals so the network, with its protocols and impairments, interferes with communication to the least degree possible. Interference with communication can take three forms. *Blockage* occurs when a terminal is denied access to the network. *Failure* occurs when a connection is established but is disrupted during transmission. *Impairment* occurs when a connection is established but provides less than ideal service: a high error rate is an example.

In this chapter we discuss the alternatives for implementing networks and strive to develop an understanding of the characteristics of such choices. The chapter is not devoted exclusively to local networks. However, since all networks share these fundamental principles, they need to be understood before one can make a selection intelligently from among the alternatives. Furthermore, local networks will seldom be self-contained. Most local networks will need access to the outside world through interconnecting circuits. Therefore, it is important to understand some of the characteristics of these external networks. Although this chapter is directed toward data networks, many of the same principles apply to voice networks as well.

DATA COMMUNICATION TERMINOLOGY

Throughout this book, we will use commonly understood abbreviations for data terminals and auxiliary devices. **Data terminal equipment,** or DTE, is an inclusive term that refers to any type of terminal, computer, or peripheral device that can be connected to a network. We will generally refer to DTE as a *terminal* or *station* because those terms are more commonly used and understood. Most terminals can communicate over a limited distance—up to approximately 50 feet—without connecting them to some form of driver or booster circuitry. This circuitry is called **data circuit-terminating equipment** (DCE). In Chapter 5 we discuss both DCE and DTE in more detail.

NETWORK RANGE

Data network designs are functions of the range the network spans between its most distant terminals. This distance is known as the network **diameter.** Local area networks are generally restricted to a diameter of about one mile or 1.6 km. The boundaries are not precise, and in fact many LANs extend much farther, but range is limited for reasons that will become apparent in our later discussions.

Networks within a geographical area about the size of a major population center are called **metropolitan networks.** They have a diameter of 10 to 20 miles. When its boundaries exceed a metropolitan area, a network is known as a **long haul** or **global network.**

IMPEDANCE

Impedance is a term encountered several times in this book, yet it is one that cannot be fully explained without delving further into the technology of transmission design, which is beyond the scope of this book. Like many other electrical concepts, impedance can be understood by a simple analogy of the flow of water through a pipe.

Just as pipes of different diameters differ in water-carrying capacity, every circuit offers some opposition to the flow of current. This opposition to the flow of current is known as the **impedance** of a circuit. When two branches of a circuit are connected, current flows smoothly if the circuits are joined through a device that matches their impedances. Visualize the turbulence that occurs when two small water pipes are connected to a larger pipe. The flow of water is disrupted least if the connection is smoothly tapered from the larger size to the smaller sizes and all abrupt changes in the direction of flow are replaced by gradual transitions. The same is true with current flow in any kind of transmission medium. This is also true of light flow in fiber optic cables.

In our discussions of local networks we will frequently be dealing with the physical interconnection of network components. With this brief explanation of the effects of mismatched impedance, it should be understood that many components cannot be wired directly together. Where impedance matching is mentioned in this book, it can be understood as the selection of electrical components to avoid disruption of the flow of electrical current by discontinuities in the circuit.

NETWORK NODES

Node is a term you will encounter frequently in discussions of networks. A **node** is the point in the network where the terminals and processors are interconnected. Nodes can be equipped with processors and, therefore, contain intelligence. They can be switching points or can provide contention-based access to the network, requiring terminals to compete with one another for capacity. A node can allow many terminals to access the network, or it can be dedicated to only one terminal or computer.

TYPES OF DATA NETWORKS

POINT-TO-POINT

The simplest network, illustrated in Figure 2.1, is the direct interconnection of terminals on a point-to-point basis. The chief advantage of a point-to-point network is its simplicity. With only two terminals there is no need for addressing. Such a network is secure. Unless the transmission medium is tapped, access to the communication is confined to the two terminals. The principal limitation of a point-to-point network is the inefficient use of capacity when the terminals are idle.

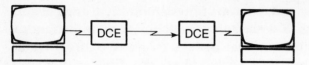

FIGURE 2.1   Point-to-point circuit

Of course, if terminal traffic occupies the network fully, efficiency is at a maximum, but if idle periods occur, there is no way of using the extra capacity.

MULTI-DROP

If a point-to-point network has idle capacity, efficiency can be improved by wiring additional terminals to the network as shown in Figure 2.2. Early teletypewriter networks used this method extensively. Today, this is one of the most common configurations of a LAN. All terminals receive all messages; in earlier networks, messages not intended for a terminal were punched on paper tape or printed and discarded. Obviously, security is poor with this method. Both security and efficiency can be improved by using address coding so the terminals respond only to messages addressed to them. Although security is imperfect with such a system, for many applications it is adequate, particularly if all users belong to the same organization, which is normally the case with local networks.

A multi-drop network has an inefficient feature similar to that of a telephone party line. When the line is occupied, other terminals must wait their turn. When the line is idle, terminals are either polled by the host or contend with one another for access. The latter networks are called **contention** networks because terminals vie with one another for access whenever the network becomes idle.

Without a network control discipline, terminal **collision** is bound to happen from time to time. In a telephone party line, collisions are annoying but endurable. In a data network, several bits of a message can be destroyed before the terminals recognize that a collision has occurred. As the contention system is widely used in local area networks, it will be discussed in detail in Chapter 10, Contention Networks.

Collisions can be reduced or eliminated with centralized or distributed control over and among the terminals. One common form of central control is **polling.** The central controller, following a predetermined algorithm, sends messages to each terminal to inquire if it has traffic to send. If it does, it is given access to the network long enough to send the message, and then it drops back to a listening state. Signaling, the reverse of polling, requires terminals to signal the central controller when they have traffic to send, and the controller determines which terminal will be given first access.

Control can also be distributed among the terminals. Then each terminal must be equipped with the network control algorithm so each can act as a master. This has the disadvantage of inflexibility. If the network requires change, all terminals must first receive a message programming them with the new access instructions. Several different methods for distributing control have been applied in LANs. The method that has been adopted as standard is **token passing.** The **token** is a software mark that circulates through the network according to a predetermined algorithm. Only the terminal with the token is permitted to send traffic, thereby eliminating the possibility of collision. We will discuss distributed control more fully in Chapter 11, "Noncontention Networks."

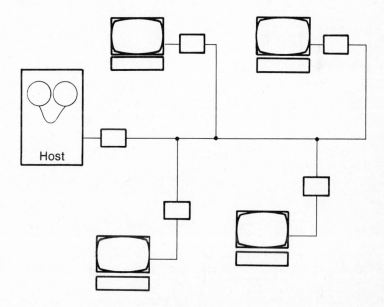

FIGURE 2.2   Multi-drop network

CIRCUIT SWITCHING

One way to improve network security and enhance network utilization is through **circuit switching.** The telephone network is the most common example. Lines radiate from a central hub to terminals distributed over a local or metropolitan area. Global networks can be accessed through a hierarchy of switching machines interconnected by **trunks.** Figure 2.3 illustrates a switched network.

The lines from the terminals to the switching system and from the switching system to other systems are collectively known as **circuits.** The central switch establishes a direct connection between terminals. During the time the terminals are connected they have the equivalent of a dedicated circuit. No data can be sent between terminals until the circuit has

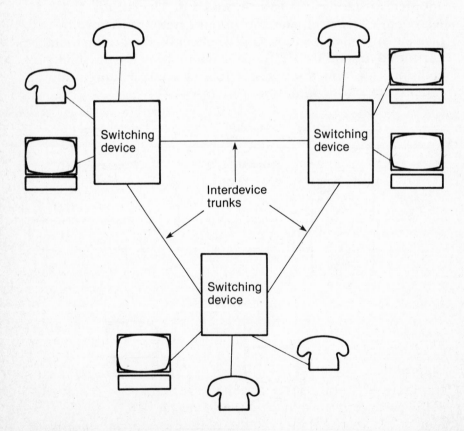

FIGURE 2.3   Circuit-switched network

been established, but once they are connected they can send data in real time. This is a significant characteristic of circuit switching because it means that data cannot arrive out of sequence.

MESSAGE SWITCHING

If a switching machine contains storage capability, it can receive a message from one terminal, store it, and forward it to the next switch, repeating the process until the message reaches the receiving terminal. With **message** or **store-and-forward** switching, it is unnecessary for the terminals to be connected to each other. Under the supervision of the central switch, receipt of the entire message is ensured. Store-and-forward switching does not necessarily imply a noticeable delay, although a delay can occur, depending on the network load and design.

PACKET SWITCHING

In a packet-switched network, control is distributed to intelligent nodes on the network, as illustrated in Figure 2.4. The terminal sends to its network access node, which breaks the message into packets, a process that is known as packet assembly/disassembly (PAD). Packet length depends on the network design, but may run from only a few to more than 1,000 bytes. (A byte is 8 bits, roughly one character.)

Each packet is preceded by a header that typically contains the address of the sending and receiving stations and the packet sequence number. The end of a packet is marked by a trailer record that includes error checking information. The message is sandwiched between the header and trailer, which are stripped off by the network protocols as the message is presented to the receiving terminal.

Two terminals in communication over a packet-switched network have a *virtual* point-to-point circuit dedicated for the duration of one packet. The packets flow between terminals over varying paths, depending on the traffic in the network. In Figure 2.4, one packet could travel from A to D over the route ABD. The next packet could travel ABCD, and so on, depending on the design of the network and the amount of traffic flowing between nodes.

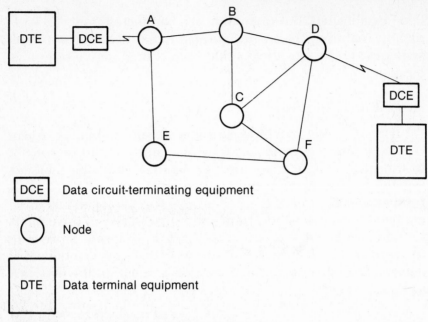

DCE	Data circuit-terminating equipment
◯	Node
DTE	Data terminal equipment

FIGURE 2.4   Packet-switched network

The network protocol can deliver data between terminals as intact messages in their original sequence. Such service is known as a **virtual circuit.** Virtual circuits can be either permanent or switched. A permanent virtual circuit is a path dedicated between two terminals, giving them the equivalent of a directly wired physical circuit. A switched virtual circuit is reestablished with each data packet. If the protocol delivers each packet as an independent unit, it is known as **datagram** service. Datagrams can arrive out of sequence, or sometimes not at all.

NETWORK DESIGN PRINCIPLES

Although the design of data networks is beyond this book's scope, we include this discussion to enhance your ability to select the appropriate design for your application. Network design relies heavily on probability and queuing theories, which you may wish to review if you want to know more about the principles supporting network design.

When a station or terminal is unable to access the network

because there is no idle capacity, the network is said to be blocked. In the case of a multi-drop network with only two terminals, obviously, there will be no blockage since these are the only two contenders for capacity. When a third terminal is added, one terminal will be blocked whenever two terminals are in communication.

If the messages are short (known as a short *holding time*), or if each terminal makes only a small number of *attempts* to establish communication, the probability of blockage is slight if the attempts fall into a random pattern. As more terminals are added and the number of attempts increases, the probability of blockage increases. If attempts are plotted against the probability of blockage, the result will fall into a pattern as shown in Figure 2.5.

Service can be improved by adding capacity to the network. In a data network, increasing the transmission speed or increasing the number of channels adds capacity. The network designer's job is to resolve the conflict of cost versus service. It is easy to bring service within acceptable limits if cost is not a consideration, or to achieve reasonable cost if service is not important, but rarely is an organization willing to disregard cost in favor of service or vice versa.

One hundred percent network efficiency is an unat-

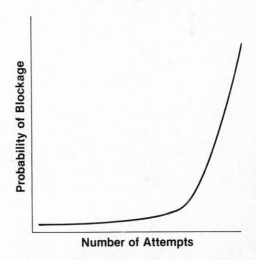

FIGURE 2.5 Probability of blockage in a network

tainable goal. Even though any network is theoretically capable of being fully occupied, perfect efficiency assumes that the contenders will send traffic in a perfectly disciplined manner. When one message is complete, another arrives at precisely the right instant to use the vacant capacity. In reality, full occupancy cannot exist. Queuing theory tells us that as efficiency approaches 100 percent, the waiting line for access approaches infinity. The designer must be contented with less than 100 percent utilization and must expect that from time to time, contenders to the network will be blocked.

NETWORK TOPOLOGY

Network **topology** or architecture is the pattern of interconnection of the terminals. The four toplogies used in LAN networks are discussed briefly in this section and in more detail in later chapters. Refer to Figure 1.1 for diagrams of the four typical topologies.

Star networks are perhaps the most familiar topology. The telephone system is configured as a star, with lines radiating from a central switching machine to individual terminals. All circuit-switched networks use this form with minor variations, in which circuits from the terminals are brought into a central switching system. Messages or packets are sent to a terminal only through the central switch over a circuit inaccessible to other terminals. In a star network access is allocated by the central controller. It is possible, as we shall see in later chapters, for terminals to be star-connected without a central switch or controller. In this configuration, the star is the electrical and logical equivalent of a bus network.

The **bus** network topology is used in the multi-drop configurations previously discussed. This is the most common configuration in LANs. Terminals are connected to a central circuit, or bus, and contend with one another for access. Messages or packets are broadcast simultaneously to all terminals on a bus. Access is either allocated by a control node, or the nodes are treated as equals and can contend for access. It is important that the open ends of a bus be terminated in their characteristic impedance to prevent reflections of data signals. In water pipe terminology a termination is equivalent to an infinitely long pipe connected to the source so that the flow is continuous.

The **ring** network is, in effect, a bus with the outer ends joined. Terminals are normally inserted in the network rather than bridged as they are in a bus, so that all messages are regenerated by each node. Control in a ring network is usually assigned to one station and is accomplished by passing a token from node to node. A control node must be designated to monitor the network for a lost or mutilated token, and to recreate the token when necessary. All nodes can contain the control logic with the first one discovering the difficulty taking independent corrective action.

The **branching tree** is similar to bus topology in that all data messages are broadcast simultaneously throughout the network. However, instead of one bus with two open ends, a branching tree can have multiple legs and as many open ends as there are branches. Care must be used in connecting the branches to avoid impedance irregularities. This is accomplished with devices known as **splitters** in cable television terminology, or by connecting legs through an amplifying device called a **repeater.** This ensures at branching points that the electrical signal is divided between two legs without the signal's being reflected back to the source. The branching tree topology is most commonly used in broadband networks using a contention access method, allowing distributed control as in a bus network.

NETWORK IMPAIRMENTS

Perfect data communication can never be absolutely assured over any form of network. For example, data errors will always occur. The technology offers intelligent design to anticipate errors and impairments and compensate through error correction procedures. The greatest impediment to data transmission is **noise.** A burst of noise that would hardly be detectable to a human ear can obliterate several data characters and render the message useless unless provisions are made for providing an error free circuit. Chapter 5 will discuss how data errors are detected and corrected.

All circuits encounter noise. In addition, they can encounter **loss,** which is a drop in signal volume between two points on a circuit. Loss is seldom a cause for concern in data transmission, particularly where circuits are provided by common carriers. In a data circuit, loss can be overcome by amplification unless the noise level is so high that the circuit is unsuited for data communication.

A third form of impairment is **echo,** which is the reflection of a portion of the transmitted energy over the receiving path. Echo is a substantial impairment to voice transmission, but is not a great concern to data transmission except over voice circuits more than 1,000 miles long. When data is transmitted over long voice circuits, it can encounter echo suppressors, which cut off transmission in the reverse direction when data is being sent in the forward direction. This prevents simultaneous two-way transmission (called *full-duplex*) unless the echo suppressor is disabled.

NETWORK ALTERNATIVES

A wide variety of alternatives is open to the user who wishes to interconnect data terminals. In the past, the majority of networks were made up of circuits acquired from AT&T or the local telephone companies, but competition has gradually entered the communications industry. The network user today is faced with a bewildering array of choices, some suitable for local network usage, and all open to consideration for interconnecting local networks.

GLOBAL NETWORKS

The most common form of global network is the public voice telephone system, which carries the bulk of data communications traffic today. Potentially, any telephone in the world can be equipped to send and receive data traffic. A world-wide addressing system has been established to enable interconnection of terminals with tolerable time delays and reasonable error performance.

Besides the telephone company, several data common carriers offer service, often over circuits leased from the telephone companies or satellite carriers. These services can offer enhancements not available on the regular telephone network such as error correction, store and forward, and protocol conversion. Because of the additional value of these services, such networks are often called **value added** networks. These networks are usually packet switched and offer such features as electronic mail and message services.

Another alternate form of global network is the privately leased or privately owned facilities supporting world-wide connections. These circuits, which can be leased from any of the common carriers, can travel over satellite or terrestrial microwave facilities.

METROPOLITAN NETWORKS

The most common metropolitan network is the switched local telephone network, which is familiar enough that it needs no discussion here. Local leased telephone circuits are also quite common. New services are being offered that can provide feasible alternatives for transmitting data traffic within a metropolitan area. Cable television (CATV) companies are beginning to offer data communication services. Most often, these are offered on a point-to-point basis, but the use of local packet switching is likely to increase in the future. As in the case of global networks, privately leased or owned metropolitan networks can be established using either leased facilities or facilities built and owned by the user.

LOCAL NETWORKS

One unique aspect of the local network is its availability to private ownership and operation. Rarely, if ever, are LANs acquired wholly from a common carrier. This means that network access and control can be selectively designed. The distances involved with metropolitan and global networks limit all but the largest organizations to using the standardized features of common carrier networks. By contrast, there is nothing to prevent you, the local network user, from installing a system uniquely suited to your needs.

3

Determining Local Network Requirements

A fundamental guiding principle for acquiring any kind of equipment or service is that you thoroughly understand your business requirements. Each organization is unique; there is no universal shopping list. We can discuss, however, some important factors to consider prior to selecting a local network.

This chapter will aid you in assessing your local network requirements. It provides the terminology you need to evaluate different products. In subsequent chapters, as we discuss local network alternatives, we will evaluate the strengths and weaknesses of the alternatives to these requirements. The primary purpose of this chapter, therefore, is to give you an understanding of the significance of determing requirements. It is not until Chapter 15 that we examine LAN requirements and specifications. At that time, we will find it necessary to review these requirements in greater detail.

RELIABILITY

The local network becomes such a vital link in the human-machine amalgam found in modern offices and factories that the effects of failure can be devastating. If one machine or one person in a system is inoperative, the system will usually continue to function, but if the entire network is out of commission, processing will halt and cost will mount. Reliability is, therefore, of paramount importance.

Reliability is an inherent function of network design and its components. Networks with central elements such as controllers and repeaters tend to be less reliable than networks with distributed control because when a central element fails the entire network is out of service. Network reliability is improved if the central elements are duplicated or redundant so that on failure a spare immediately takes over. With other factors equal, those networks where control is distributed to the nodes are inherently most reliable because failure of an element will affect only one node.

Reliability is usually quoted in terms of percent availability, which is a function of two factors, **mean time between**

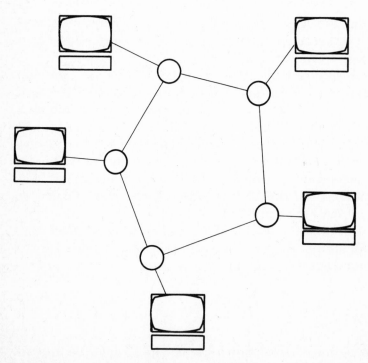

FIGURE 3.1   Ring network

failures (MTBF) and **mean time to repair** (MTTR). MTBF can be stated in any unit of time and provides a clue to how frequently you can expect a failure. To illustrate, consider the ring network in Figure 3.1. The manufacturer quotes an MTBF of 100,000 hours for each node. As there are 8760 hours in a year this means a node will fail, on the average, about once in 11 years. This seems acceptable, but note that the network has 5 nodes in series. As any one of these could fail at any time in an 11-year period, the network MTBF will be 11/5 or approximately 2.2 years. Furthermore, other circuit elements such as the cable, fittings, and power supplies have expected failure rates of their own, so the failure rate of the entire network will be considerably greater than the failure rate of the nodes. Moreover, software failures can be virtually impossible to predict.

The method of calculating MTBF is based on average failure rates of the equipment, and within a reasonable range it is accurate. As a purchaser, your task is to determine how much faith to place in the manufacturer's estimate. One way to gauge this is to ask for documentation supporting field experience, preferably users' verifiable results.

Another important element in reliability is mean time to repair (MTTR), which is the average time it takes to restore a failed system. Because this time is highly dependent on the location and skills of the repair force, you should inquire closely into how accurate the estimates are. Generally, MTTR presumes a trained technician, and either none or an average amount of travel time. MTTR is not an absolute guide to how long it will take to repair a failed network, but it can be a good indication of the differences among products.

The percent availability of a network is derived from the formula:

$$\frac{\text{MTBF} - \text{MTTR}}{\text{MTBF}} \, (100)$$

For example, if a network has an MTBF of 1000 hours and an MTTR of 4 hours, the availability would be (1000 – 4)/1000 = 99.6 percent.

MAINTAINABILITY

When the local network fails, (or "goes down") as it inevitably will, it is important to restore it as quickly as possible. You should inquire into factors affecting restoral time with such questions as:

- How well is the network documented? Does it come with sufficient technical information for a knowledgeable technician quickly to locate and correct the trouble?
- Are spare parts readily available? Are they available commercially, or does the manufacturer use proprietary parts?
- How long, based on experience, can the vendor be expected to support maintenance on the network?
- Are vulnerable elements duplicated for increased reliability?
- How accessible are the vendor's repair forces?
- What experience have other users had with repair of the network?
- Does the network include internal diagnostics to aid in locating trouble rapidly?
- Does the network include central elements that can cause the entire network to fail, or does it fail gracefully, one node at a time?
- Is the network designed and built to survive in my operating environment? For example, does it include elements that are sensitive to dust, noise, shock, vibration, or external electrical disturbances?
- How long will the vendor support it after new designs are released?

Maintainability and reliability are inseparable factors. If the network is highly reliable, maintainability becomes less important, but if reliability is questionable, you'll need to be prepared to repair it as quickly as possible.

DATA THROUGHPUT

The speed of data transfer or throughput is a result of many diverse factors in designing a total system. The productivity of network users will be affected by throughput. Ideally the network should impose no limitations beyond those imposed by the terminals and computers. Several factors should be considered in evaluating the actual network throughput.

BANDWIDTH

Bandwidth refers to the range of frequencies that can be accepted over an analog network, or the data rate in bits per second over a digital network. Bandwidth is a function of the transmission medium and of the data modulation methods. Of the commercially available services, speeds from 50 b/s, which is suitable for low-speed telemetering, to more than 1.5 mb/s can be obtained, while keeping the cost proportional to both data rate and circuit length.

An ordinary telephone voice channel passes frequencies from 300 Hz to 3000 Hz and, generally, can pass data reliably at speeds up to 4800 b/s. Specially designed or conditioned voice channels can carry data rates up to 19.2 kb/s over limited distances. Other transmission media can accommodate much higher speeds. Coaxial cable will handle data rates of more than 10 mb/s and analog signals up to 400 mHz. Fiber optics can handle data rates over 500 mb/s with currently available technology.

ACCESS METHOD

The terminal access method is a critical factor in determining throughput. Dialed-up networks are generally slow, the dialing time becoming a significant portion of the total connect time. Multiple access contention networks require little signaling time, but if the load is beyond the network's carrying capacity, throughput will be reduced because of collisions and repeated access attempts. Token networks have more predictable throughput than other alternatives.

NETWORK LOAD

All networks are sensitive to load. As we discussed in the last chapter, when the load approaches the theoretical capacity of the network, delays increase until at 100 percent of capacity, delays are infinite. In evaluating a local network, carefully inquire about the load capacity of the network, and compare this to the load you plan to impose.

DATA TRANSFER RATE

Data transfer rate is independent of bandwidth. Regardless of how much bandwidth is available to a network, data transfer speed can be limited by the design of circuit elements. For example, if you have a 4800 b/s voice channel, but DCE capable of only 1200 b/s, the data transfer rate cannot exceed the capacity limits of the DCE.

ERROR RATE AND RECOVERY METHOD

A data channel with a high error rate will have a lower throughput than an error-free channel because much capacity can be consumed in detecting and correcting errors. The error rate is dependent on the design of the channel, the channel's exposure to external influences, and the transmission medium used. For example, a fiber optic system is practically immune to errors from external noise, and is therefore a good choice in a noisy environment. The shielding of coaxial cable is an effective way to reduce errors caused by noise, while twisted pair cable is susceptible to most kinds of interference.

PROTOCOLS

Protocols will be explained in greater detail in Chapter 6. For now, consider that they contain overhead bits that facilitate data transmission; they do not add to the information content. An inefficient protocol can consume a great deal of the network's transmission time in error detection and correction, message logging, and other such functions. Most protocols function by sandwiching a message between header and trailer records. Therefore, the ratio of the length of the protocol to the length of the message will affect throughput.

CAPACITY OF THE NETWORK

Closely related to throughput and data transfer speed is the capacity of the network. Capacity is a function of the number of communication channels, the speed of each channel, the length of data messages, the time between messages, and the number of terminals that are offering traffic to the network. One way of evaluating capacity is to inquire into the effective data transfer rate of the network. For example, if a network has a data transfer rate of 10 mb/s, given the nature of your data traffic the vendor should be able to predict the effective throughput rate. Be prepared, however, to make your own independent evaluation. Throughput will be less than the theoretical maximum after overhead bits have been stripped off, errors corrected and collision recovery accomplished. From a knowledge of your data traffic you can then calculate whether the network has enough capacity to handle your load.

RANGE OR NETWORK DIAMETER

As we discussed in the last chapter, network diameter is the distance between the two most widely separated terminals on the network. If the diameter is more than a mile this will virtually eliminate high-speed, multiple-access bus networks from consideration. At short ranges the cost of multiplex for point-to-point circuits becomes prohibitive compared to other methods. To achieve the desired range with a wide diameter you may be forced to use multiple networks connected by a gateway or bridge.

INTERFACING EXTERNAL NETWORKS

In some applications local networks are complete within their own bounds and have no need to communicate with other networks. For example, many closed-loop manufacturing processes have no requirement for external communications. However, where people are interactive with central computers and data bases and with other terminals, off-net communication is often required.

Distance limitations can be overcome by bridging networks together. Although most broadband and circuit-switched networks have enough range to span a good-sized campus or industrial complex, baseband networks impose restrictions that would eliminate them from consideration without a means of splitting them into subnetworks and bridging them to other networks.

A second reason for interconnecting networks is the need to link dissimilar networks. For example, an organization might need to connect a broadband contention network to a PBX for access to the public telephone system. Differences in communications requirements might also necessitate interconnecting networks. One unit might have bursty traffic that is ideally suited to a baseband contention network, while another unit might have priority traffic that requires the use of token passing. These two dissimilar networks may require access to each other for certain types of traffic.

Right-of-way may also become a limiting factor in expanding the network. An organization may have two facilities separated by a street, a river, or other intervening property with no right-of-way. It is impossible to serve such a situation with a single LAN. Separate networks will be required with some means such as radio, optics, or common carrier facilities to bridge the two together.

Separate organizational units can require separate networks to preserve security or to ensure that one organization does not suffer delays because of the coinciding traffic peaks of another. Networks can also be split as a load-sharing strategy to group terminals with common interests. In some cases, clusters of terminals can have a large amount of traffic among one another, but little to other networks. The use of multiple networks is a way of equalizing the traffic load.

There are two basic methods of interconnecting networks. A **gateway** circuit communicates with the two networks through each network's protocol. A gateway is needed for each pair of networks. A second method is by use of a **bridge.** A bridge interconnects networks through higher level protocols. Contrasted to a gateway, which communicates by using each network's own protocol, the bridge allows the protocols to coordinate, accommodating any difference between the two, and makes the protocols appear compatible.

COST

Cost is a most important consideration to users. However, don't be lulled into installing a local network on the basis of price alone. The important factor to consider is the magnitude of total cash flows resulting from ownership of the network over its service life. The important factors to consider are:

- Conversion costs
- Total installation cost
- Maintenance and upkeep
- Software enhancements
- Lost production time during outages
- Life of the technology
- Long-term vendor support

In selecting a local network you should quantify these cash flows as accurately as possible. The last one on the list is somewhat difficult to quantify, but for the remainder, you should be able to make a reasonable estimate of how much money you will spend during the time you own the product. In Chapter 16 and in Appendix B we explain a process for evaluating total or **life cycle** costs of a local network.

FLEXIBILITY

Some types of local network are limited to data transmission while other networks can handle voice and video as well. If your organization has no need for other services, flexibility will not be an important factor.

Another aspect of flexibility, which we discuss in the next section, is how a local network can be expanded after reaching maximum capacity. Some networks can be expanded to keep up with growth of the organization, while others must be duplicated to add capacity. You should compare your long-term requirements with the capability of the network to determine how flexible it is.

EXPANDABILITY

When acquiring a local network, most organizations are entering an unfamiliar area of distributed data processing or office automation. Consequently they initially have no precise understanding of how to satisfy their company's ultimate requirements. As an organization grows, more terminals and peripherals are required. If growth is inhibited by capacity, and if the network cannot be expanded, productivity will suffer. Acquiring a local network requires some long-term planning: it is important to consider the network's ultimate size and the vendor's solution toward future expansion.

NONPROPRIETARY TERMINALS

Unfortunately, a characteristic of the computer industry is the lack of compatibility among equipment made by competing manufacturers. Often, an important reason for acquiring a local network is to achieve the compatibility necessary to interface various devices. As an organization expands into a new application area, it seldom can afford to discard its existing equipment.

For most applications, it is important that the local network be able to support a wide variety of terminals. One effective way is to acquire a network that conforms to a recognized standard. (More about standards in Chapter 4.) If the network conforms to no standard, the vendor should provide specific information regarding compatibility with other manufacturers. Otherwise, you will be limiting your choice of terminals and devices for the life of the network.

If the organization is expected to expand, you should consider future requirements when selecting the network. If, however, the network will be located in a single building with little likelihood of exceeding those bounds, range should be the least consideration in selecting alternatives.

VENDOR SUPPORT

It is important to know whether the vendor will be readily available when you need assistance. Here are some questions to consider:

- How available is the repair force?
- What kind of support does the vendor offer in keeping the network upgraded with enhancements? What is the charge for upgrades?

- Is the vendor likely to join the list of failing data equipment manufacturers?
- What kind of warranty service does the vendor offer?
- What kind of technical assistance is available? Is it available on a 24-hour basis, or only eight hours per day—perhaps only five hours if the vendor is on the opposite end of the continent? (It is expensive to equip and maintain a user support force. Minimizing user support is one way some vendors offer a product for a lower price than their competitors.)
- What is the vendor's reputation among users for supporting a product once it is sold?
- Does the vendor offer full support features such as engineering and installation of the network?

SUMMARY

This chapter provided an overview of some of the most important factors to consider when selecting a local area network and the vendor. With this information and with terminology acquired in the next two chapters, you will be prepared to evaluate the multitude of alternatives that face you when you enter the market for a local area network. After we have examined the alternatives, we will use and enlarge upon LAN requirements to develop a network system unique to your organization.

4

Local Network Standards

If you've ever tried to accumulate a set of tools, nuts, bolts and screws to work on automobiles, you can appreciate the problem of multiple standards. Small machine screws are designated arbitrarily with the numbers 2, 4, 6, 8, 10, and 12. The pitch is expressed in the number of threads per inch with 28 and 32 threads being common. Beginning with 1/4-inch bolts, the diameter is measured in 1/16-inch increments, and threads are designated as national coarse or national fine. Bolt heads are measured in 1/16-inch increments. With foreign automobiles and a few U. S. models, the diameter, threads, and heads are measured in metric dimensions.

With computer communications, the problem is even worse. Lacking standards, manufacturers have set their own. Often manufacturers design their equipment to be compatible with that of a manufacturer dominant in the industry, but frequently compatibility with a *standard* is not absolute. For example, the X.25 standard supported by the Consultative Committee on International Telephone and Telegraph (CCITT), which we will discuss shortly, is intended to be an international standard for interfacing equipment to a packet-switched network. However, the standard includes so many options, that even though a product is designed to support X.25, compatibility between different equipment is still not assured. This lack of compatibility makes it difficult to connect systems made by different manufacturers. Communication between devices is in the best case hampered, or in the worst case, impractical for the average user.

In an ideal world, standards would precede technology. Once a technology was proved feasible, a standard would develop to encourage manufacture of compatible products. Unfortunately, the competitive world doesn't work that way. A technology is proved feasible only when it has been tested in the field, revised, improved, and accepted by the users. Finally some recognized authority or representative agency develops a standard.

Because there are so many ways to implement a data communications network, contradictory opinions on the nature of the standard are interjected into the process. After wide debate, a consensus begins to emerge. Although it won't satisfy everyone, at least a standard represents an accord of some of the best minds and talents that industry and government can bring to bear on the problem.

Local area networks have undergone such an evolution. While standards have evolved, they are by no means the last word, and there is no assurance that they will gain widespread acceptance, for compliance with standards is completely voluntary. Before we look at local network standards, let us first review the principal standard-setting organizations and discuss their roles in the process.

STANDARD–SETTING ORGANIZATIONS

By its nature, telecommunications transcends national boundaries. The value of both voice and data communications is proportionate to the growing number of terminals that can communicate, and the development of international commerce in equipment and systems. The value of communications is enhanced when it is able to cross national boundaries. Therefore international agreement on protocols is required.

INTERNATIONAL TELECOMMUNICATIONS UNION (ITU)

The ITU is a specialized agency of the United Nations with headquarters in Geneva. Its purpose is to facilitate international communications by setting standards and implementing treaties among the member nations. A further objective of the ITU is to promote international trade by setting standards that apply in any country.

The ITU consists of two major consultative committees: one on radio and one on telecommunications. Its work is done by technical representatives from both government and industry and by a staff funded by voluntary contributions from the participating nations.

The Consultative Committee on Radio (CCIR) is involved in frequency allocations and international regulation of radio transmission to prevent interference.

Of greater importance to data communications and local area networks is the work of the Consultative Committee on International Telephone and Telegraph (CCITT). With wide participation from ITU members, CCITT prepares recommendations for communications standards, including data communications. The recommendations are just that. Compliance is voluntary, although manufacturers have considerable incentive to adapt their equipment to the recommendations unless they are large enough to establish standards of their own.

Of particular interest in data communications are the X series and V series of CCITT recommendations, which are listed in Appendix A. The X recommendations relate to data communications within digital networks. The most prominent recommendations for data communications are X.25 and X.21, which we discuss in Chapter 6.

CCITT recommendations are developed by participating representatives from the member nations. In the United States participation is almost exclusively provided by the private sector. Well-qualified individuals hold positions as rapporteurs on topics the CCITT is considering. As a result of this participation, important issues are thoroughly aired and acceptable standards are developed, although often not in time to prevent influential manufacturers from developing standards of their own.

INTERNATIONAL STANDARDS ORGANIZATION (ISO)

The ISO is a sister organization to ITU, but is not limited to establishing telecommunications standards. The national standards organizations of the member nations comprise its membership. One of its important functions is standardization of digital data transmission techniques. A major standard of ISO from a data communications standpoint is the Open Systems Interconnection (OSI) model for data communications (described more fully in Chapter 6). The OSI model consists of a seven-layer protocol, which has been widely adopted with modification by many other standards organizations. For example, CCITT X.25 protocol uses the first three layers of the OSI model. The link layer of X.25 is identical to ISO's High Level Data Link Control (HDLC).

AMERICAN NATIONAL STANDARDS INSTITUTE (ANSI)

ANSI is the American standards organization that coordinates with ISO and the ITU. One of ANSI's responsibilities is to set communications standards. ANSI draws widely from other U. S. standard-setting organizations through its task groups. The OSI model of ISO was developed as a result of an ANSI-sponsored project to develop a distributed processing model.

ELECTRONICS INDUSTRIES ASSOCIATION (EIA)

The EIA is a manufacturer's organization that recommends standards for interconnection between equipment made by different manufacturers. Examples of EIA standards are the RS 232-C, a familiar interconnection standard between DCE and DTE, and the replacing recommendations RS 422 and RS 423. The RS 232-C interface is similar to CCITT V.24.

INSTITUTE OF ELECTRICAL AND ELECTRONIC ENGINEERS (IEEE)

The IEEE has been influential in setting standards to enhance data processing and data communications. For example, the IEEE 488 computer bus has been a standard used by many manufacturers over the past ten years. The primary motivator in setting local area network standards was the

IEEE 802 committee. We discuss their work later in this chapter.

FEDERAL COMMUNICATIONS COMMISSION (FCC)

The FCC is not a standard-setting agency as such, but through its regulatory activities, it exerts a strong influence on rates and technical standards. The FCC also specifies the interconnection point between operating telephone companies and users of data communications equipment.

LOCAL AREA NETWORK STANDARDS

Local area network standards began in much the same way as other communications standards did. Manufacturers experimented with communications and access techniques, developed numerous proprietary techniques, and gradually demonstrated the feasibility of local network access methods. But most manufacturers developed their own proprietary protocols, limiting the compatibility between the network and existing equipment and that of other manufacturers.

One network that became widely accepted as a standard was Ethernet. Created in the early 1970s by Xerox Corporation in its Palo Alto Research Center, the network proved to be a successful method of allowing mutliple users to access a high-speed network. Xerox collaborated with Digital Equipment Corp. and Intel in developing Ethernet before promoting it vigorously as a standard. To encourage acceptance of Ethernet, the standard was openly published and offererd for licensing at a nominal cost. However, although Ethernet is satisfactory for certain types of data traffic, its inability to support heavy and long messages prevents its universal acceptance.

THE IEEE 802 COMMITTEE

In 1980 the IEEE Computer Society appointed a committee to work on project 802 for the development of local area network standards. The 802 committee's overall objectives, which have largely been met, were to establish standards for the physical interconnection of devices to local networks, and the data link between devices. With many alternatives to consider, the 802 committee developed specific objectives to focus their activities into an achievable project. The following requirements have become established standards* for local area networks (Graube, 1982):

- Application is light industrial and commercial functions, excluding heavy traffic and home use.
- The diameter or distance between terminals is up to 2 kilometers.
- The network configuration supports up to 200 devices on a single cable.
- Data rates can be from 1 mb/s to 20 mb/s.
- The network can be supported by various transmission media.
- The network system ensures that there will be no more than one undetected error per year, and that the failure of any single device on the network should not degrade the entire network.
- Existing data communications standards should be incorporated into the IEEE standard as much as possible.

The requirement that no single device should cause the network to fail eliminated circuit switching from consideration. Although at first the committee had hoped to set a single network standard, contention networks using Ethernet techniques imposed limitations that were unacceptable for many applications. Therefore, the committee set two noncompatible standards. For light applications a bus contention network similar to Ethernet was selected. Where assurance of network access is needed, token passing bus and ring standards were selected.

The 802 committee completed its work on bus standards in 1982 and put them out for comment. The IEEE adopted the standards in 1983, and a few weeks later ISO announced that it would initiate proceedings to standardize the 802 format.

The 802 standards are published in five parts:*

---

*Copies of the standards can be purchased from the IEEE Computer Society, 10662 Los Vaqueros Circle, Los Alamitos, CA 90720.

802.1 Document containing the reference model, tutorial, and glossary.

802.2 Link Layer Protocol Standard

802.3 Contention Bus Standard

802.4 Token Bus Standard

802.5 Token Ring Standard

The 802 standards do not encompass all the functions needed to implement an entire network. The standard is developed around the ISO layered protocols, which are described more fully in Chapter 6. In a layered protocol, the functions needed to establish a total application from one end to another are established in discreet packages that are usually called *layers*. The ISO Open Systems Interconnection model specifies each layer's function, but work is not yet complete in standardizing the protocol of each layer. Therefore, although a network may conform to one of the 802 standards, this does not mean that equipment is interchangeable between networks; as yet, the 802 standard is composed of only the first two layers of the ISO model.

Furthermore, although the IEEE standards have been announced, many nonconforming products are on the market and will continue to function outside the realm of IEEE standards. There is no reason nonstandard networks should not be considered if they fulfill your requirements. However, a primary drawback to using a network that does not conform to the standard is that you may have difficulty obtaining compatible equipment sometime in the future; you may be limited to dealing with one vendor. The day of the universally compatible data terminal is still in the future. In the meantime, progress is being made toward standardization.

5

A Minicourse in Data Communications

Before you can understand how local networks operate, you need a working knowledge of data communications technology and its terminology. In this chapter, we will review some important concepts. If you already have a good grasp of the fundamentals of data communications, you may want to skip this chapter. If you have no background in data communications, you may find that the explanations here are not sufficient in detail. In that case, you may need more information on data communications. The Bibliography at the end of the book lists references that will help you gain a more complete understanding.

BINARY COMMUNICATION TECHNIQUES

If you were to trace the etymology of the word *digital*, you might conclude that its use relative to a computer is a misnomer, for digital is derived from the Latin word for finger. While we have ten digits on our hands, a digital computer can manipulate only two values, zero and one. The machine's tremendous strength is its ability to process numbers made up of these two values extremely fast. However, one weakness is the computer's inability to transmit its output directly for more than about 50 feet without data circuit-terminating equipment.

Inside the computer the two digits of the binary numbering system, "0" and "1," are assigned different voltage levels. Each BInary digiT, or **bit** represents the smallest unit of information that can be stored and processed by a computer. Alphabetic characters, decimal numbers, and special characters are represented by binary codes made up of unique combinations of eight bits, known in computer vernacular as a **byte** or an **octet.** For example, in computer language, the letter *A* is represented by 01000001. For a computer to communicate with an external device, a character or number is gated through logic circuits to an output **port.** If a peripheral device is close enough, it can be directly coupled to the computer. For longer distances, the physical characteristics of the telecommunications medium distort the output pulses so that zeros and ones can't be distinguished from one another. To overcome these effects, some form of output driver or booster is required.

Within the transmission limits of twisted-pair copper wire, a simple line driver suffices to transmit the computer's output signal. For longer distances such as over telephone lines, the computer's digital output must be converted to analog form, the only type of signal most long distance telecommunications circuits are capable of handling. Digital-to-analog conversion is accomplished with a device called a **modem,** which is derived from the words MOdulator-DEModulator.

Unlike a digital signal, which consists of discrete pulses of voltage of two different levels, analog signals are analogous or proportionate to the modulating signal. Figure 5.1 illustrates how modems can vary the amplitude, frequency, or phase of their output in response to the modulating signal. Special modems are available to couple a terminal or computer to any kind of telecommunications medium.

When computers process data, they manipulate the bits in **parallel.** That is, the eight bits of a byte travel over eight separate paths through the machine at the same time. Computers with 16-and 32-bit paths are in widespread use on the market, but their output characters are still in eight-bit bytes, and as the eight-bit machine is easier to visualize, we'll confine our discussion to that for the time being.

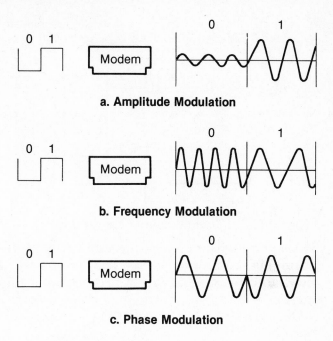

a. Amplitude Modulation

b. Frequency Modulation

c. Phase Modulation

FIGURE 5.1   Modem modulation techniques

Connecting eight separate paths to peripheral equipment is feasible if the distances are short. For longer distances, it is more economical to use a single path and convert the output to *serial* form. The parallel-to-serial conversion is accomplished in a chip known as a Universal Asynchronous Receiver-Transmitter (UART). Figure 5.2 illustrates the concept of parallel-to-serial conversion. When a computer receives data, the process is reversed and the incoming serial signal is converted to parallel.

Terminals require some means of marking the start of each new byte. Without this synchronizing method it would be easy to lose track of where one byte stops and the next one begins, thus garbling communication hopelessly. Two forms of synchronization are used. The simplest form, **asynchronous** (often called *start-stop*), uses a start bit to mark the beginning of a byte and a stop bit to mark its ending. With **synchronous** communication, data is sent in blocks between sending and receiving devices synchronized by a clock signal. Figure 5.3 illustrates the two synchronizing methods. Syn-

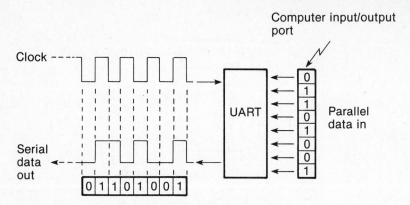

FIGURE 5.2　Parallel-to-serial conversion

chronous communications are discussed in more detail through our examination of protocols in Chapter 6.

CODING SYSTEMS

The zeros and ones of computer output are coded into a pattern that must be recognizable by the receiver. The most common coding system is the American Standard Code for Information Interchange (ASCII). ASCII is a seven-bit code, meaning that characters are encoded in arrays of seven bits. This gives the code a total of 2^7 or 128 discrete combinations. The eighth bit in the ASCII byte is used for error detection and correction.

A second code commonly used today is the Extended Binary Coded Decimal Interchange Code (EBCDIC), which is an eight-bit code used by IBM and other manufacturers. Numerous other codes are also in use, but since they are outside the scope of our topic, we will not discuss them in this book. The important thing to keep in mind is that for devices to communicate, they must be capable of handling the same coding scheme. Most "dumb" terminals are inherently configured for one code and cannot easily be changed. Programmable terminals, computers, and many local networks can be programmed to handle code translation.

ERROR–DETECTING METHODS

No telecommunications system is capable of operating without errors. In the telephone system, impulse noise occurs from switch and relay operations in older types of switching devices. Microwave radio and fiber optic systems can open the circuit for an instant when switching from a regular to a standby channel. Even local networks that are not subject to public access are bound to be interrupted occasionally. Noise enters a system from a multitude of sources, and each burst of noise results in data errors. A protocol should at least inform you that an error has occurred, and in the best case will notify the sender to retransmit until the data is received without error. In this section, we will review the basic concepts of error detection and correction, and we will enlarge on them in the protocol discussion in the next chapter.

PARITY CHECKING

In this simple form of error detection, also known as **vertical redundancy checking** (VRC), one bit of the coded byte is designated as a parity bit. Parity can be set as odd or even, referring to the number of "one" bits in the byte. For example, if you are using even parity, when sending the letter "A," which has an even number of "one" bits, the parity bit would

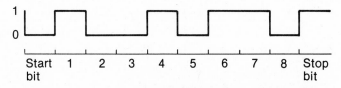

Start 1 2 3 4 5 6 7 8 Stop
bit   bit

a. Asynchronous Transmission

Flag	Address	Control	Variable length information field	Check field	Flag

b. Synchronous Transmission

FIGURE 5.3   Data synchronizing methods

be off or zero. The letter "C," which has an odd number of "one" bits would be sent with the parity bit set as "one" to create an even parity state.

When a noise burst strikes and destroys an odd number of bits, the receiving apparatus can detect that an error occurred. Most simple terminals on the market today are capable of this type of error detection. VRC works well, but it has a serious weakness. If an even number of bits is damaged, the error will pass undetected. A more sophisticated error-checking system is needed.

LONGITUDINAL REDUNDANCY CHECKING

Longitudinal redundancy checking, or LRC, is one method of overcoming the drawbacks of VRC. Data is sent in blocks, and the parity of each bit position is checked for all the bytes in the block. The last byte in the block is a parity byte that sets the bit position to even parity (or odd if odd parity is specified by the designer). Figure 5.4 illustrates the use of this system. LRC requires a more elaborate protocol and more intelligence in the terminal than VRC, but it is more reliable. If a block is received with an error, the sending terminal can be requested to resend the block until it is received error free.

| | | \multicolumn{6}{c}{Data Characters} | Block Parity* |
		1	2	3	4	5	6	
	1	0	1	0	1	1	0	1
	2	1	1	0	0	1	1	0
	3	0	1	0	1	1	0	1
Bit position	4	0	0	1	0	1	1	1
	5	1	0	1	1	0	1	0
	6	0	1	0	1	0	1	1
	7	1	0	1	0	1	1	0
	p*	1	0	1	0	1	1	0

Direction of Transmission ⟶

*Even parity

FIGURE 5.4   Longitudinal redundancy checking (LRC)

CYCLICAL REDUNDANCY CHECKING

Although LRC is more reliable than VRC, it is still incapable of consistent error-free performance. Most protocols use a more elaborate system known as cyclical redundancy checking, or CRC, to enable the detection of virtually all errors. With CRC, the data message is processed at the transmitting end against a complex polynomial. The result of the calculation is transmitted to the receiving end where a similar calculation is made, and the two results are compared. As with LRC, when an error is detected, the receiving terminal requests the transmitting terminal to resend the block.

DATA TRANSMISSION SPEEDS

The data communications industry has standardized a range of transmission speeds optionally available to meet the user's objectives based on data rate and cost. Speeds of 50, 150, 300, 1200, 2400, 4800, 9600, 19,200, and 56,000 or 64,000 b/s are widely used, with occasional requirement of intermediate speeds such as 1800 and 7200 b/s. Higher speeds up to 1.544 mb/s are commercially available for high-speed data transfer, video, or for submultiplexing to lower speeds. Figure 5.5. shows the range of speeds supported by different digital transmission applications.

You will often hear the terms *bits per second* and *baud* used interchangeably. From a user's standpoint, you can consider them synonymous without getting into trouble, but there is a distinct difference between the two. The term baud can be remembered by thinking of it as a contraction to the phrase "Bit of AUdio Data." (Actually the term was named after the same J. M. E. Baudot for whom baudot code was named.) The baud rate of a channel refers to the number of times per second the channel is capable of reversing the state between zero and one. Referring back to Figure 5.3, you will observe that an asynchronous channel changes state ten times for each byte even though only seven information bits are transferred. The other three bits are used for stop, start, and parity and contribute nothing to the information transmitted over the channel.

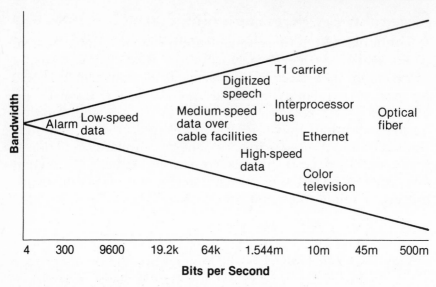

FIGURE 5.5   Data transmission bandwidth requirements

The baud rate of a channel is limited by its bandwidth. A telephone channel, for example, is limited to 2400 baud by filters that are inherent in its design. However, this does not limit the number of bits per second the channel can carry to 2400. Sophisticated modems using phase shift techniques are capable of sending more than one bit per baud. For example, 4800 b/s modems send two bits per baud, and 9600 b/s modems send four bits per baud. Under ideal conditions those speeds can be transmitted over an ordinary telephone circuit.

In data communications it is essential that the sending and receiving devices both be capable of operating at the same speed, or that they communicate through a device that offers speed conversion. Many local networks can accept data from a terminal at one data rate and store it in a buffer for transmission to another terminal at a different data rate.

DISTANCE LIMITATIONS

The cost of data communications rises in direct proportion to transmission speed and distance, although some of the costs can be offset by using less sophisticated equipment over limited distances. For example, many common carriers offer a limited distance data service (LDDS) of 19.2 kb/s within a range of one to two miles from the serving central office.

One method for improving the range of a digital circuit without the use of analog modems is to regenerate the pulses before they deteriorate to the point that errors occur. Pulse regenerators are sometimes known as **repeaters.** In ring networks, for example, pulses are regenerated at each node, allowing more distance between terminals than with systems lacking regeneration.

HALF– AND FULL–DUPLEX

Systems that are capable of transmitting in both directions at the same time are known as **full-duplex.** With **half-duplex** systems, transmission is possible in only one direction at a time. In most interactive applications, full-duplex transmission is required, but in many applications, such as batch transmission from a computer to a remote printer or remote job entry from a terminal to a computer, only half-duplex transmission is needed.

Full-duplex operation is accomplished either with two separate circuits operating in opposite directions simultaneously (known as *four-wire*), or by using a **split channel modem.** In split channel operation, used by most asynchronous modems operating at 1200 b/s or less, the frequency band of the transmission medium is divided into two equal segments, one for each direction of transmission. Some modems are equipped with a narrow band reversing channel so the transmitting terminal can be interrupted by the receiver. A terminal can use the full channel bandwidth to transmit in one direction, then be reversed to transmit in the other.

MULTIPLEXERS

The term *multiplex* is an ambiguous term in telecommunications. As it is a term you will encounter often, its different meanings will be explained here so you will be able to distinguish between the uses. In its broadest sense, the term means the derivation of more than one communication channel over a single transmission medium.

Common carriers use multiplexing to divide a transmission medium such as twisted-pair cable, coaxial cable, microwave radio, or fiber optic cable into multiple voice grade channels. (A voice grade channel occupies a frequency band from 300 to 3000 Hz in analog systems and supports 64 kb/s speeds in digital systems.) Analog multiplexers use a technique known as **frequency division multiplexing,** which divides the transmission medium into frequency segments 4 kHz-wide by an analog **carrier** system. A set of miniature transmitters and receivers tuned to fixed frequencies is used to carry an analog signal. The filters in these systems limit the bandwidth of a telephone channel and impose an upper limit on the data speed the bandwidth can support.

Digital or **time division multiplexing** assigns each channel to a *time slot* and divides the base channel into discrete time segments by a process known as **pulse code modulation** (discussed in more detail in the next section). Multiplexing techniques in use today can add a minimum of one channel to a single pair of wires and more than 8000 channels on a pair of optical fibers.

Data multiplexers are used to subdivide communications channels to further improve their data carrying capability. To illustrate the simplest kind of multiplexer, assume two points: A and B are linked by a single circuit capable of carrying 4800 b/s. Suppose, however, that a pair of terminals connected to the circuit are capable of transmitting only 1200 b/s. To link these terminals with 4800 b/s circuits obviously wastes a great deal of circuit capacity. A multiplexer utilizes this capacity by dividing the circuit into four 1200 b/s slots or subchannels. Thus, four pairs of 1200 b/s terminals can communicate over a 4800 b/s circuit without interfering with one another. Figure 5.6(a) illustrates this type of multiplexing.

Because of the nature of data traffic, circuit capacity remains unused with data multiplexing. Unless the circuits are operated with simultaneous transmission in both directions, and unless the terminals are transmitting continuously, there will be idle time available. A *statistical multiplexer* uses this idle time by assigning a terminal to a channel only when it has traffic to send. The statistical multiplexers send data messages be-

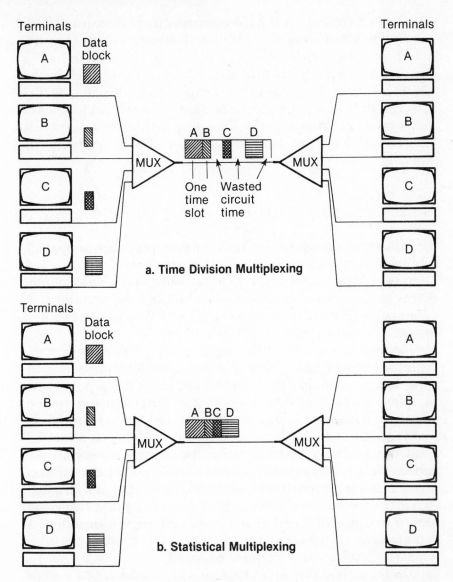

FIGURE 5.6 Multiplexing techniques

tween themselves indicating which terminal a block of characters is intended for. Figure 5.6(b) illustrates statistical multiplexing.

With statistical multiplexers, a great deal of circuit concentration is available. The actual number of terminals that can be assigned to a circuit depends on the bandwidth, the terminal's transmitting speed, the nature of the data transmitted, and the distribution of the traffic. If the traffic is evenly distributed, statistical multiplexing can make efficient use of a channel. However, if the traffic is characterized by high peaks and low valleys, the channel can experience blockage. Statistical multiplexers collect information to assist a circuit administrator in adjusting the load to provide the maximum amount of carrying capacity with a low probability of blockage.

PULSE CODE MODULATION

Pulse code modulation, or *T carrier,* plays an important role in some forms of local network. It is useful for creating point-to-point circuits over a broadband transmission medium. Because we refer to PCM techniques throughout this volume, we discuss the basic principles of PCM in this chapter to serve as a foundation for future discussion.

Figure 5.7 is a conceptual diagram of a T carrier system. When a voice signal enters a PCM channel unit, its analog wave form is sampled at a rate of 8,000 times per second. The sampler can be conceptualized as a rotating distributor (the circuit is actually electronic). Each sample has an amplitude that is identical to the amplitude of the voice signal at the instant of sampling. The output of the sample enters an encoding circuit that creates an eight bit-word (or byte if you prefer) that is proportional to the amplitude of the original signal. The word travels through repeaters or pulse regenerators to the receiving end of the circuit where it is decoded. A gating circuit distributes it to the appropriate channel decoder where its analog wave shape is restored.

Each channel operates at a speed of 64 kb/s (8 bits × 8,000 samples/second). A T carrier system interleaves 24 such channels to create a 1.544 mb/s signal (64 kb/s × 24 channels plus some framing bits). The signal thus created, also called a DS-1 signal, can be transmitted over two pairs of twisted copper wires, one for transmitting and one for receiving. Regenerators are placed at 6,000-foot intervals to ensure that the received wave shape is identical to the transmitted signal.

As the system is designed, it is usually equipped only for

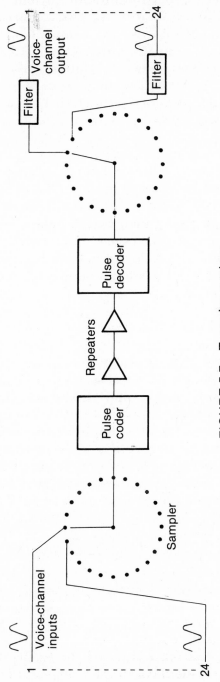

FIGURE 5.7   T carrier system

analog inputs. Therefore, even though T carrier is digital, to send a data signal over a T carrier system requires the use of a modem. The data signal is sampled on an analog basis and restored to an analog signal at the distant end. Obviously, with the 2400 baud limitation of a voice channel, this wastes the 64 kb/s-capacity of a T carrier channel. In private line applications, direct digital inputs of up to 56 kb/s can be accommodated by replacing a plug-in voice channel with a special purpose channel.

T carrier systems are beginning to have wide application in data communications. Currently, most channel banks are located in common carriers' central offices where they are used to multiplex voice and data channels between other central offices. As higher transmission speeds are required, users will increasingly terminate leased T carrier lines on their premises where among other uses, they can link local networks together at speeds as high as 1.5 mb/s.

SUMMARY

We have covered a great deal of data communications terminology in a short space. Because it is essential to understanding how local networks operate and can be used, you may want to review the information in this chapter from time to time as we discuss the different alternatives for local networks. Although a local network is a specialized application of data communications, the techniques described here are used in typical local network applications. This discussion should aid in understanding them.

6

Network Protocols

In diplomacy, protocols are the conventions people follow in conducting the affairs of state. Although diplomats have customs and languages unique to their own country, a common language has evolved to facilitate universal communication. But everyone must observe standard rules. Much the same objectives characterize data communications.

With the diverse origins of data communications equipment, it became evident that protocols or *handshaking* was needed if different devices were to communicate with each other. To communicate, devices must have compatible interfaces, identify which device transmits on low frequency and receives on high frequency of a modem, determine what transmission speed to use, recognize and correct errors, terminate the connection, and must satisfy any other such requirements that precede the exchanging of data.

ASYNCHRONOUS DATA PROTOCOL

The simplest protocol is that used for asynchronous communication. Between two permanently attached devices, the shift from a stop bit to a start bit is enough to prepare a device to receive the next character.

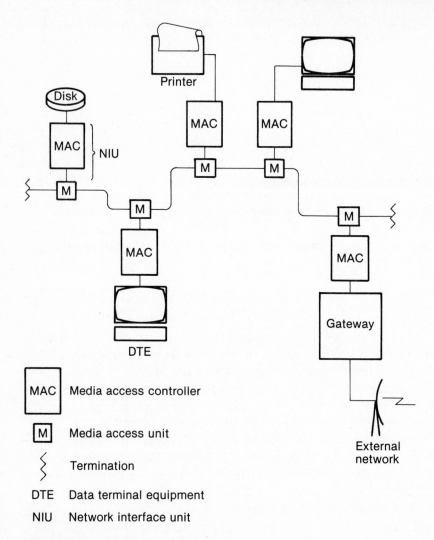

FIGURE 6.1   Local area network

If the device attachment is temporary and communicating devices are switched onto a voice-grade line, more activity is needed to establish a connection. The sending DTE must signal its intention to send, and on receiving a go-ahead message from its DCE it must send the address (telephone number) of the receiving terminal. When the receiving terminal is signaled, its DCE must verify that the DTE is prepared to receive messages. The receiving DTE informs the transmitting DTE that the circuit is established for communication.

This exchange of signals takes place over an interface, commonly RS 232-C or RS 449, between the DCE and DTE.

SYNCHRONOUS PROTOCOLS

At higher speeds, asynchronous protocols have limitations that reduce the throughput of a circuit. The start and stop bits in each character are an overhead that uses circuit capacity without contributing to the exchange of information. It is more efficient to use a synchronous protocol in which characters are transmitted in blocks with only the overhead of the header and trailer records. Most of the major data equipment manufacturers have developed their own synchronous protocols. While they resemble one another in function, they are different enough to be mutually incompatible.

Local area networks commonly communicate between nodes with synchronous protocols, but the nodes often communicate with their attached terminals in an asynchronous mode. Figure 6.1 is a diagram of a simple LAN: Terminals are attached to the network through a **network interface unit** (NIU) that consists of a **media access controller** (MAC) and a **media access unit** (MAU). The network is connected to external networks through a gateway or bridge. A terminal will likely communicate with its NIU at 1200 or 2400 b/s. The NIU will communicate with the network at a considerably higher speed, often 10 mb/s. The user is unaware of the operation of the protocol. Its purpose is to provide the user with a virtual circuit to the distant terminal.

THE ISO MODEL

When data communications came into widespread use, computer manufacturers developed proprietary protocols to allow their own devices to communicate with each other. The result was incompatibility. Often, one vendor's devices could not communicate with another vendor's devices. In an effort to provide a structure for developing standards, the **International Standards Organization** (ISO) developed a model for layered control of communications over a data network: the

Open Systems Interconnection (OSI) model is shown in Figure 6.2.

Protocol functions designed around the OSI model are divided into layers. Controlling communications in layers adds some extra overhead because each layer communicates with its counterpart through header records. However, layered protocols are easier to administer than simpler protocols and provide opportunity for standardization. Although protocols are complex, functions in each layer can be modularized to allow system engineers to deal with the complexity in each layer separately.

Layered control offers an opportunity for standardization and interconnection between the proprietary architectures of different manufacturers. Generally, the degree of standardization is greatest at the first layer and becomes increasingly disparate in the higher layers. Finally, the last layer, the application itself, is largely without standardization among vendors.

The objective of the OSI reference model is to establish a framework that will allow any conforming system or network to connect and exchange signals, messages, packets, and addresses. The model makes it possible for communications to become independent of the individual manufacturer. It should be understood that although the OSI model can be used to develop standards, it is not a standard itself. Later in this chapter we discuss how the IEEE 802 committee applies the OSI model to the development of LAN standards.

In the OSI model, the first three layers describe the interfaces between terminals and a shared network. Layers four to seven describe the end-to-end connections between software during a session. The functions within each OSI layer are described below.

Layer 1—Physical.   The first layer establishes the method of physical interconnection over a circuit. The physical layer is concerned with the transmission of bits between devices and with the standardization of pin connections between DCE and DTE. Typical standards are CCITT V.24 and X.21, and EIA RS 232-C and RS 449.

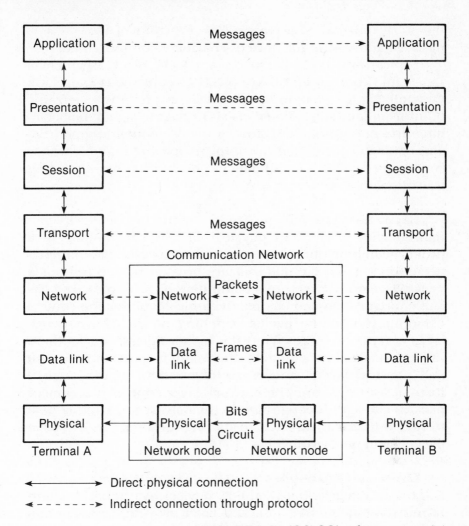

FIGURE 6.2   ISO OSI reference model

Layer 2—Data Link.   Data link protocols concern the transmission of data frames between terminals. The protocol in the data link layer detects and corrects errors to provide the user with an error-free circuit. The data link layer takes raw data characters, creates data frames, and processes acknowledgement messages from the receiver. When frames are lost or mutilated, the logic in this layer arranges retransmission. Protocols contain flags and headers to allow DTE to recognize the start and end of a frame. One function of this layer is message addressing for devices sharing a common link.

Typical link layer protocols are ISO's HDLC (High-Level Data Link Control) and IBM's SDLC (Synchronous Data Link Control). Figure 5.3(b) in the previous chapter shows a frame of information. The frame consists of flags to signal the beginning and ending of the frame, a header containing address and control information, an information field, and a trailer containing cyclical redundancy check bits for detecting transmission errors.

Layer 3—Network. Modern computer networks configured with other than physical circuits can operate in a packet-switching mode. Network devices can be interconnected by virtual circuits that are created by the flow of a packet stream between two computers or terminals. The circuit configuration can change dynamically under the control of computers in the packet-switching nodes. The network layer accepts messages from the higher layers, breaks them into packets, delivers them to the distant end through the link and physical layers, and reassembles them in the original form of transmission. The network layer controls the flow of packets and avoids congestion in the network by routing data to nodes that can direct it to its final destination. A typical packet switching protocol is CCITT X.25.

Layer 4—Transport. The transport layer controls end-to-end integrity between DTE devices by establishing and terminating the connection. This layer provides essential network management functions for data transmissions over various types of network systems. For example, networks can be configured from point-to-point terrestrial circuits, satellite circuits, or common carrier packet-switching networks, each supporting different characteristics. The transport layer provides a standard service regardless of the characteristics of each network. It accomplishes this function by communicating through message headers and control messages with its corresponding transport layer in the remote device.

Layer 5—Session. The user communicates directly with the session layer. The session layer converts the user address to that required by the transport layer. The conventions for the session are established in this layer. For example, the validity of the parties can be verified by passwords or other conventions. The session can be established as a full-duplex or a half-duplex session. The session layer determines whether devices can interrupt one another. It establishes how to begin and terminate a session, and how to restore the connection in case the session is interrupted by failure. The session control is generally established by the manager of the network, and once the user elects to use the network, the session protocols of the proprietor must be observed.

Layer 6—Presentation. This layer interprets the character stream that flows between terminals during the session. If encryption is required, for example, the presentation layer will provide it. If bit compression is used to conserve transmission time, this layer will support it. Other machine control functions such as skipping, tabbing, form feed, and cursor movement are presentation layer functions.

Communication between word processors, for example, is a presentation layer function. Special characters are used for cursor control, page formatting, skipping lines, and other such functions. The presentation layer can communicate these special functions between word processors.

Layer 7—Application. The application layer, which is specified by the user, defines the task being performed. For example, in facsimile communication, the task would be to transmit a page of information between two terminals. The application is highly specialized and unique to the vendor and the user, resulting in little in the way of standardization.

THE X.25 PROTOCOL

Of more than passing interest to LAN users is CCITT's X.25 standard that describes the interface between a computer and a packet switching network. The X.25 standard is based on the first, second, and third layers of the OSI model. To discuss its development is an instructive experience in itself.

CCITT developed the X.25 protocol for use as a synchronous standard interface between the user and a packet network. Although X.25 is not used directly within a local network, it is important to understand it for two reasons. First, it employs typical protocol functions and thus illustrates the purposes of a protocol. Second, it is necessary to understand something of X.25 to understand how a local network can interface to an external network, since most public networks have adopted varations of X.25.

The X.25 protocol consists of three layers of the OSI model: the physical, the link, and the network layers. The physical layer interface is the X.21 standard, a relatively new digital interface that is not yet widely available. An interim standard, X.21 bis, is nearly identical to RS 232-C and more commonly used.

The link layer uses HDLC to control packet transfer, to control errors and to establish the data link. The third, or network layer, provides two types of channels between equipment: One is a **permanent virtual circuit** (PVC) that offers the equivalent of a leased end-to-end channel by predefining a fixed routing through the network; the other is a **switched virtual circuit** (SVC) that establishes routing with each packet.

The primary use of X.25 is to connect between a host mainframe and a public packet switched data network. Presently there are few terminals that support X.25 interfaces. For an individual terminal, the major packet carriers offer dial-up access to their networks, but the major advantage of end-to-end error correction is lost. Large commercial users can interface public packet networks in one of three ways: over a carrier-certified software interface, a carrier-supplied interface processor that resides on the user's premises and connects to the user's computer, or through a user-supplied packet assembler/disassembler (PAD).

X.25 is a protocol that is far from static. It has undergone two major revisions since its provisional introduction by CCITT in 1974. Little commercial use was made of that issue. It was revised again in 1980 to add numerous options that were not included in earlier versions. The implications of the options in X.25 are significant for local network users. Although many local networks offer gateways to X.25 networks, it is important to determine that the versions of the protocol are compatible.

THE PURPOSES OF A PROTOCOL

At this point, let's pause to summarize the purposes of a protocol. To begin with, the protocol establishes compatibility between devices; each machine knows exactly what to expect from the other. The protocol also establishes the line discipline: that is, whether the session is half-or full duplex and what the signals mean on the circuit. Another protocol function is to set up and terminate connections. For example, if the connection is to be billed, the protocol signals the billing equipment to start at the moment the connection is established. The protocol can assist in error detection and correction. By enabling message blocks to arrive out of sequence, the receiving terminal can recognize the error and deliver the packets in the proper sequence. The protocol is the main defense against mutilated or out-of-sequence messages.

ESSENTIALS OF PACKET SWITCHING

We have alluded to the concepts of packet switching and virtual circuits several times in this book. It is time to develop these concepts more fully as a way of understanding local networks because local networks must switch terminals together by circuit switching (i.e. connecting the terminals with a physical circuit) or packet switching (i.e. connecting terminals through a virtual circuit).

As we saw in Figure 5.3b, a data frame sandwiches a group of information characters between header and trailer records. The principle is much like marshalling railroad cars in a railway yard. A certain amount of cargo is loaded into each car. Then the cars are coupled together and switched onto the appropriate track for the journey to their destination.

Suppose an originating terminal wishes to send a message to a receiver over a packet-switched network. The message can be any length—it makes no difference to the network. The terminal media access controller (MAC) receives the message, breaks it into packets of the correct length, calculates a cyclical redundancy check block for error checking, assigns the message a sequence number, and at the appropriate instant sends it on the network. In the network illustrated in Figure 6.1, all nodes receive the message, but only the addressee accepts it and forwards it to its terminal. The others simply discard the message.

The receiving MAC performs several checks before passing the message on to its terminal. It ensures that it arrives error free. If there is an error, the MAC sends a message to the transmitting terminal to retransmit the block. It checks that the block arrives in the correct sequence. If out of sequence, the MAC will store it until the preceding blocks are relayed to the terminal. The objective of the process is to make the entire message transmission transparent to the terminals.

Packet switching is more complicated when the terminals are not all wired to the same bus. In the ring network illustrated in Figure 6.3, when a node that is not the addressee receives a message it regenerates the message and passes it to the next node on the network.

Many long-haul packet data networks operate on the prin-

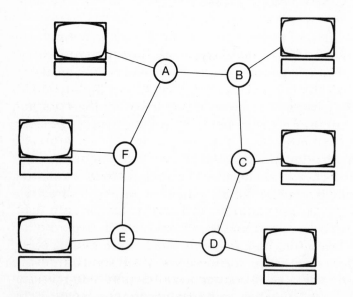

FIGURE 6.3   Ring data network

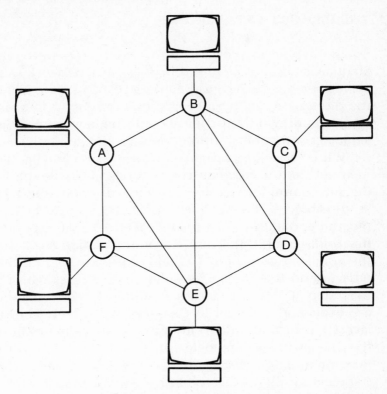

FIGURE 6.4   Packet-switched data network

ciple just described, although they will likely be configured with a more complex array of circuits like the "mesh" network illustrated in Figure 6.4. As node A has no direct connection to node D, it decides (based on its knowledge of the configuration and load on the network) whether to pass its traffic to node B, E, or F. These nodes, in turn, select the best routing to node D. The packet flow through a network such as this is constantly changing because a route that is blocked at one instant can be free at the next.

It is easy to see how a packet can take a shorter path than its predecessor and arrive out of sequence. Likewise, a momentary disruption in a network can cause a packet to be delayed or lost. A protocol compensates for the disturbances on the network and gives the user a connection to the distant user that is as error-free as if the two were connected by a short cable.

THE IEEE 802.2 STANDARDS

In Chapter 4 we briefly discussed the role of the IEEE 802 Standards Committee in setting local area network standards. In this chapter, as well as Chapters 10 and 11, we will enlarge the discussion on these standards in order to increase your understanding of how they act with higher protocol layers to achieve compatibility among devices and systems.

With the wide variety of transmission media, signaling methods, and access control methods available for LAN use the 802 committee developed standards to be as independent as possible of the network structure. The 802 committee recommendations, shown in Figure 6.5, correspond to the first and second OSI layers. Recommendation 802.2 describes the link layer control (LLC) that is common to both the token passing and the Carrier Sense Multiple Access with Collision Detection (CSMA/CD) access methods—access methods that are explained in detail in Chapters 10 and 11. The physical layers can accommodate either a coaxial or fiber optic cable in the bus and ring topologies. In this chapter we will discuss Recommendation 802.2, (the LLC) which relates to the 802.3 standard for CSMA/CD, the 802.4 standard for the token bus, and the 802.5 standard for the token ring access methods.

The 802 standards divide the second layer of the OSI model, the data link layer, into two portions: the LLC and the media access control (MAC). The reason for this division is to standardize to the greatest degree possible the interface between the layers. Because there is so little commonality between the MAC functions of token passing and CSMA/CD access methods, the functions that are common have been extracted and implemented in the LLC.

The LLC communicates with the network layer and the MAC sublayer through *primitives.* Primitives are an abstract method of describing functions that must be performed in communications between layers. Only the *service* required between layers is contained in the primitive. The method is left up to the manufacturer of the network.

The LLC communicates with the other layers through three types of primitives. The *request* primitive is used by the higher layers to initiate a service providing action. The *indication* primitive is used for a lower level to communicate an

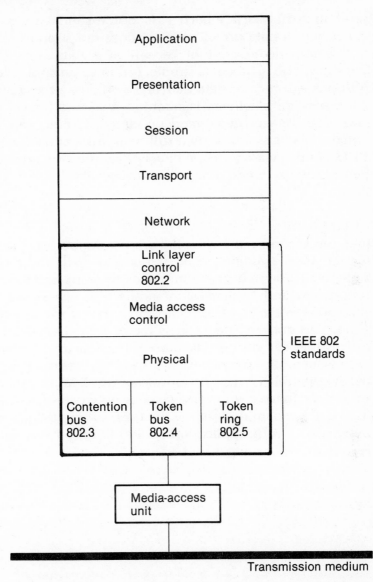

FIGURE 6.5   IEEE 802 local area network standards

event of significance back to the higher layer. A *confirmation* primitive is used by the lower layer to communicate the results of a service request back to the user through the intermediate layers.

The 802.2 standard supports two classes of data links: The first type, a *data link connectionless* or datagram service, is used in a network where it is not essential to guarantee delivery of a data unit. This class does not support flow control, acknowledgement of receipt of a data unit, or error recovery. The protocol is simple, but in some applications the lack of assurance of data delivery would be unacceptable.

Where data delivery is essential, a second type of service, *data link connection-oriented* or virtual circuit, can be provided. This class supports a full data link protocol similar to HDLC. In this class a virtual data link connection is established before the exchange of information occurs.

SUMMARY

As you evaluate local networks, it is important to remember that many networks may be using access methods, topologies, and transmission media that are similar to the IEEE 802 standard but, in reality, do not conform in significant ways. This does not necessarily mean the network will be unsatisfactory for your application. It does mean, however, that the performance characteristics and the interconnectibility to 802 compatible devices cannot be assured. Moreover, keep in mind that there is an entire class of network—circuit switching—that is not addressed by the IEEE standard—and an ideal network for your application could fall into this category.

7

Transmission Media for Local Networks

The choice of transmission medium for most local network systems is limited to what the vendor offers. Because the performance of the network greatly depends on the performance of the transmission medium, you should be familiar with what is available. In some applications the availability of a particular transmission medium can be the deciding factor in choosing which network to buy.

Several factors must be considered, however. One is the transmission medium's capability to withstand electrical interference from external sources. Another factor is network throughput, which is limited by the transmission medium's bandwidth; you must choose the appropriate bandwidth from the range of alternatives that vendors offer. Bandwidth, in turn, is limited by the system length, and some transmission media can function over longer distances than others. Finally, but not least in the consideration of an appropriate transmission medium, is its capability to support multiple access: Some media lend themselves to multiple access more readily than others. And this leads to yet another consideration—user security. Some media can be tapped easily, while others are quite secure. In this chapter we will review the alternatives available on the market and discuss the strengths, weaknesses, and typical applications of each.

TWISTED-PAIR OR RIBBON CABLE

The earliest networks, beginning with the first telegraph systems, used copper wire to interconnect stations. Even today, twisted-pair wire is inexpensive, readily available, and adequate for many local network applications. In fact, most circuit-switched local networks rely heavily, if not exclusively, on twisted-pair wire to connect terminals. However, the use of twisted-pair wire for LANs has its drawbacks.

To discuss the advantage first, wire is inexpensive. You can purchase it off the shelf. It requires little technical skill to install and connect wire. Installation requires simple and inexpensive hand tools. Its bandwidth can handle high-speed data circuits. For distances up to three miles, you can transmit 64 kb/s signals over twisted-pair wire without amplification.

Twisted-pair wire is manufactured in a variety of configurations, ranging from one pair to several hundred pairs of wire in the same sheath. It also comes in flat ribbons for installation under carpet. In plastic-sheathed cable it can be pulled through plenum chambers, false ceilings, and conduits, exposed along baseboards, or concealed under the floor. It is durable and capable of withstanding considerable abuse without damage, and with its sheath intact, it is impervious to weather.

Despite its advantages, this type of wire limits LAN applications. For example, as we mentioned previously, its bandwidth is too narrow to tap for multiple access in high-speed networks, and it is highly susceptible to interference. Unless cable is shielded, electrical impulses from external sources such as elevators and industrial equipment can cause data errors. However, in a circuit-switched star or point-to-point configuration, the limitations of twisted-pair can be overcome. It is in bus and ring topologies that its limitations restrict its use to a few low-speed applications.

An understanding of the reasons for the limitations of twisted-pair wire can be useful when it is time to select a local network. For example, Figure 7.1 shows how a data signal is transmitted over wire. When a signal leaves the transmitting DTE, the pulses are square and perfectly shaped. As the signal travels down the wire, distortion begins to round the shoul-

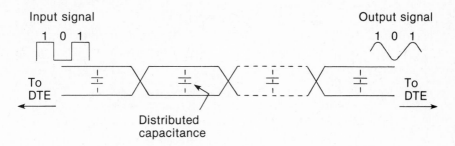

FIGURE 7.1   Data pulse distortion over twisted-pair wire

ders of the pulses. The distortion occurs because of the wire's inherent characteristics (capacitance and inductance), which cause it to filter out the high frequency components of the pulses. For error-free performance, the receiving DTE must be able to distinguish between zeros and ones in the data signal. Because of this pulse rounding, the signal must either be regenerated before it deteriorates, or the circuit length must be limited to the maximum that will enable error-free transmission.

Some small amount of noise is always present on any medium, so it is important that the level of the data signal be higher than the level of the largest noise pulses. At higher data rates, pulses are narrower, and the effects of pulse rounding become more severe. Therefore, higher speeds are more susceptible to error and require more frequent regeneration than lower speeds.

The amount of interference from external noise is related to the degree of *balance* of the cable pair. Imbalance can occur when the two wires are not electrically identical. Imbalance is caused by poorly designed cable (it is important that the wires be twisted precisely), by poorly designed taps or terminal equipment, or by wiring errors when the cable is installed.

Figure 7.2 shows the effects of imbalance in paired wire. The DCE receives data pulses by detecting the voltage across the two wires of a cable pair. If wire is perfectly balanced, external currents flow equally in each wire and remain undetected by the DCE. When the wires are unbalanced, however, the interfering signal flows unequally and results in an un-

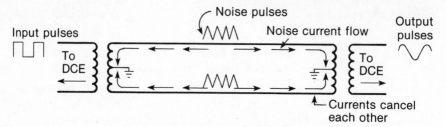

a. Noise Current Flow in a Balanced Line

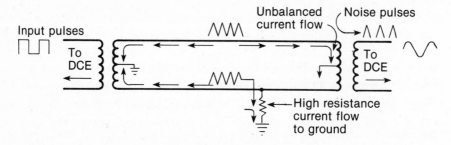

b. Noise Current Flow in an Unbalanced Line

FIGURE 7.2   Noise current flow in balanced and unbalanced transmission lines

wanted voltage between the wires. When the unwanted voltage is high enough to trigger the detector in the DCE, a data error results. Shielding can reduce the degree of influence of the noise, but in metallic circuits, the poorer the balance, the more susceptiblity to noise. Shielding is often not enough to overcome the effects of poor design and construction.

Applications.   Typically, twisted-pair wire supports low-speed LAN applications, as well as circuit-switched networks (we discuss these in the next chapter). The circuit switch within a network can be a central computer or a PBX system with terminals connected over paired or ribbon cable. When wiring point-to-point configurations with no need for multiple terminal access, twisted-pair wire is an adequate and economical means. However where security is important, copper cable is a poor choice, for it is easily tapped and taps are difficult to detect.

COAXIAL CABLE

Currently, LANs are using coaxial cable (coax) more than any other transmission medium. It is inexpensive, offers a wide bandwidth, and is not difficult to install. It supports video and high-speed data on both point-to-point and multiple access networks. Coax is widely used for cable television (CATV). It is manufactured in large quantities and marketed through many sources.

The center conductor is a single copper wire, although some LANs use cable with two or three conductors, known as twinaxial and triaxial cable. The center conductor(s) is insulated by foam, plastic, or by plastic or Teflon discs spaced at regular intervals. The outer shield is either a semi-rigid copper or aluminum tube or a flexible braid. An outer PVC or Teflon jacket completes the cable. When the cable is properly installed, the outer shield isolates the center conductor from noise impulses, creating a medium that is reasonably free from noise. Coaxial cables with flexible shields are inexpensive and easy to install, but their electrical characteristics are not as closely controlled as cables with a solid shield. Don't assume that local networks are capable of operating over the inexpensive coax that you can buy in any electronic store. You should follow the LAN manufacturer's recommendations, which may require cable that is costly, rigid, and difficult to install.

Coaxial cables have a bandwidth up to 400 mHz and are capable of handling both high-speed data and video. Technicians with moderate training can install and connect coaxial cable. The tools for installing coax are not expensive, but unless the work is carefully done an impedance irregularity can result, impairing the operation of the LAN. Coax can be tapped with little difficulty. Figure 7.3 illustrates a fixture that clamps to the outer sheath and pierces the center conductor to connect terminals to a bus network. In some LAN systems, a skilled technician can tap the coax without interrupting service to working terminals.

Data signals are imposed on a coax in either a **baseband** or a **broadband** form. With **baseband** modulation, the process for applying signals directly to the coax is similar to the

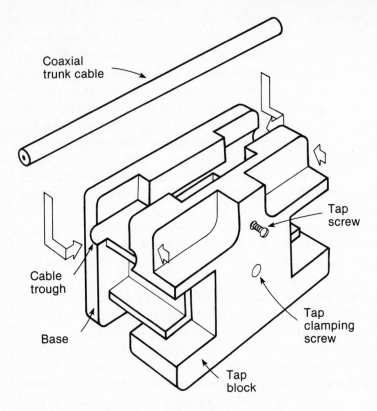

FIGURE 7.3   Coaxial cable tap connector

process used with twisted-pair wire data transmission. (Figure 7.1 provides an illustration.) A single message is carried at one time. Coax is manufactured to strict specifications and therefore is capable of handling much higher data rates than twisted-pair wire. The IEEE 802 standards support data rates up to 20 mb/s on coaxial cable.

The other means of modulating coax with a data signal is **broadband.** The techniques are similar to those used by cable television for imposing multiple channels on one cable. Radio frequency (RF) carriers are coupled to the cable and are detected by frequency selective apparatus in much the same manner as a television receiver selects among multiple channels. The different channels can be assigned to data, voice, and video communications.

The primary disadvantage of coaxial cable networks is

their requirement for special drivers to use the entire band-width of the cable. Where twisted-pair wire can be driven at low speed with inexpensive drivers, special transceivers are needed to access coax. If coax is to be multiplexed for broad-band use, a topic we will cover in Chapter 13, RF modems are needed to modulate the data, voice, and video signals on the RF channels. Baseband coaxial cables are also susceptible to interference if their sheath is grounded in more than one place. Special precautions are required to insulate cable con-nectors from ground.

Applications.   Coaxial cable supports a wide range of applications in the local network. Presently, the majority of baseband and broadband LANs in offices and industrial loca-tions use coax. Any application requiring high speed and im-munity to interfering signals must use a medium with wide bandwidth and shielding. Only coaxial cable and fiber optics can meet these requirements.

Coax can be used in any of the topologies, although it is unlikely to be economical in a star network. When security is needed, coaxial cable is a reasonably good alternative. While communications on the network are not secure from unau-thorized access, the coaxial cable itself is difficult to tap without being detected.

FIBER OPTICS

In the late 1970s, fiber optics or *lightwave* emerged from the laboratory and rapidly gained acceptance as a transmis-sion medium for metropolitan and long-haul circuits. As costs decline, lightwave will become an important medium for local area networks as well.

Fiber optic conductors are tiny *pipes* made by depositing layers of a pure silicon substance on the inner surface of a glass tube about three feet long and 1 1/2 inches in diameter. When the deposition is completed, the tube is collapsed under heat and drawn into a thin strand of highly transparent glass. The optical characteristics of a glass fiber are so precise that a light signal entering one end of the fiber can travel for a mile and exit with nearly the same intensity.

A fiber optic transmission system consists of a light source that is either a laser or a light-emitting diode that is about the size of a grain of salt. The light source emits a coherent beam of light. Coherence means that the light rays are parallel to one another. The light source is triggered on and off at a very high rate. Light pulses travel down the fiber and are detected by a receiving device that is usually equipped with an avalanche photo diode. At the current state of the art, signals more than 500 mb/s can be transmitted over a fiber optic system. As we indicated in Chapter 1, at this rate the entire Encyclopedia Brittanica can be transmitted in four seconds.

Obviously, few organizations need to transmit this quantity of data or textual information. Many organizations do, however, have a requirement for voice and video transmission, which consume much larger amounts of bandwidth than data signals. For example, at the current state of technology, a digitized broadcast grade video channel requires 1.5 mb/s, although video of a lower quality can be transmitted at one-half to one-third that speed. When data, voice, and video requirements are integrated, many organizations may require the bandwidth of fiber optics for a local network. Moreover, as the cost declines, fiber and lightwave equipment will be competitive with coaxial cable for lower bandwidth applications.

FIBER OPTIC MODES

When glass fibers first emerged from the laboratory, their loss, or the amount of attenuation of the light from one end to the other, was high. This meant that regenerators were required at frequent intervals, adding to the cost, and thus limiting the feasibility of fiber optics as a transmission medium.

The loss is not only the result of lack of transparency of the glass, it also comes about because of reflection of light waves as they travel down the fiber. Light waves glancing from the walls of a fiber take a longer path than waves that are emitted in a straight line. With some light waves arriving slightly out of phase with other rays in the same pulse, rounding of the pulse occurs. Before the point is reached where zeros and ones can no longer be distinguished, the pulse must be regenerated. A new generation of fiber, known as *single mode,* greatly reduces these multi-path reflections and allows much greater repeater spacing than with the older *multi-mode* technology.

FIBER OPTICS CHARACTERISTICS

Lightwave has two characteristics that make it ideal for data transmission. First, it is immune to noise from external sources: Because signals are carried as light pulses, electromagnetic signals cannot disturb a data signal. Second, optical fiber has an enormous amount of bandwidth. With multimode fiber, terminals can be as far apart as six miles and still provide reliable communication without a repeater. With single mode fiber the reliable communication distance can be 30 miles or more without regenerating the signal.

Offsetting the advantages of fiber optics are several disadvantages that limit its applications in LANs. First, a lightwave system is expensive. The cable drivers use a combination of electronic and light technology and are more costly than coaxial cable drivers. Next, fiber cable cannot be worked with ordinary hand tools. It requires special apparatus to splice glass fibers and precision to align a fiber with its connecting light transceivers.

Furthermore, glass fibers are difficult to tap. Although this is an advantage for security, it renders fiber optics almost unusable in a bus topology. It can, however, be used in a star in which all fibers are linked at a central point, creating the equivalent of a bus. It can also be used in a ring configuration, with each node regenerating the light signal.

The technology of fiber optics is changing so rapidly that any disadvantages that apply today may have been overcome by tomorrow. Many companies are researching the technology, and prices are rapidly declining. Fiber optics will be an increasingly important technology of local area networks in the future.

Applications. Like coaxial cable, fiber optics is advantageous in any application needing high bandwidth and noise immunity; moreover, it is superior to coax in both of these respects. Its application is limited to a star or ring topology. For applications where high quality and high speed are required, fiber optics is unlikely to be equaled. For networks requiring maximum security, fiber is an excellent choice because it is difficult to tap without being detected.

MICROWAVE RADIO

The cable technologies have a common drawback—where streets must be crossed and moderate distances spanned, right-of-way can be costly. This makes radio an attractive candidate for linking local networks together, or for linking the local network with distant terminals. Microwave radio is inherently a point-to-point medium. As microwaves travel in a straight line, intermediate stations can be linked only if they are on the path of the radio beam. However, security is poor with radio. It is impossible to prevent unauthorized detection of data signals over a microwave path although the data can be encrypted to improve security.

Collisions are a stumbling block to using microwave in a contention network. An early network using contention access was the University of Hawaii's Aloha network. Chapter 10 describes this network as well as the cause of contention problems in radio.

Microwave is expensive to purchase, requires trained technicians to install and maintain, and is susceptible to interference from outside sources. Because the radio frequency spectrum is limited, it may be difficult to obtain licenses to operate a microwave system.

Applications.   The main application of microwave in a local network is to link networks together through gateways and extend a local network to distant terminals.

OPTICAL TRANSMISSION EQUIPMENT

Optical transceivers can operate over line of sight distances, such as crossing a street between two buildings. The applications for this equipment are primarily confined to extending a local network or to bridging two local networks where right-of-way is difficult to acquire.

TABLE 7.1   Comparison of Transmission Media Characteristics

Trans- mission Media Types	Cost	Multi- Access	Band- Width	Net- work Diam.	Inter- ference immunity	Security	Ease of Instal- ation
Wire	1	2	3	3	3	3	1
Coax	2	1	2	2	2	2	2
Fiber	3	3	1	1	1	1	3

1 Most attractive choice
2 Less attractive choice
3 Least attractive choice
Note: Microwave and optics are omitted from this table because of their limited applications

Although it has been used successfully where continuous operation was not an absolute requirement, optical equipment is subject to severe limitations that restrict its use in local networks. It is subject to attenuation from rain, fog, birds, dust and other interfering objects. Since light travels in straight lines, the transmitter and receiver must be precisely aligned. Security is difficult to assure, although the narrow beam of light will show a drop in intensity whenever it is interfered with, so tapping attempts can usually be detected. Its application will be limited to short distances where other alternatives are prohibitively expensive. Even with its limitations, cost consideration will make it an attractive alternative for certain applications.

SUMMARY

As with other aspects of the automated office, the selection of the transmission medium should start with a searching analysis of your own requirements. You should pay particular attention to the noise influence in the environment, the need for security, the throughput requirements, and the distance between terminals.

Cost, of course, is always a factor. Efficiency of multiple access and ease of tapping a working system to add nodes are also imporant considerations. Table 7.1 matches local network requirements to the performance of each of the media alternatives.

8

Circuit-switched
Local Networks

In a circuit-switched network, a switching system resides at the hub of the network with terminals radiating in a star topology. When two terminals or stations are connected through a circuit switch, they are given a full time channel for the duration of the connection. The switch can be a private branch exchange (PBX), a time shared computer, or a data switch designed for the purpose. A variety of terminals ranging from telephones to computers can be wired from remote locations to the central switch, usually with twisted-pair wire.

With circuit switching, terminal-to-terminal connections are not time-shared with other users as they are with packet switching. With the virtual circuits of a packet-switched network, it is possible for packets to arrive out of sequence, or sometimes to be lost entirely. One advantage of circuit switching is that data cannot be lost or arrive out of sequence. A second advantage is that both voice and data can be switched through a single device. Although local area networks are capable of handling voice traffic, most LANs are inefficient handlers of voice, compared to circuit switches.

Compatibility of data terminals with the PBX is rarely a problem. The PBX communicates with the terminal only to set up the connection. In fact, if a telephone is available to establish the connection through the switch, the terminal and the PBX are never in direct communication. After the connection is established, the terminal communicates with the distant end through a transparent connection that is limited only by the bandwidth of the data channel through the switch.

In any organization that has an existing PBX, circuit switching is an economical way of adding a few terminals. Compared to the cost of adding a paralleling LAN, the incremental cost of adding terminals to an existing switching system is often negligible. Furthermore, circuit switching is capable of operating over a wider range than many LANs. Where a LAN using contention access can operate over a diameter of about 1,500 feet, PBXs using limited-distance modems can transmit data at 19.2 kb/s over a radius of more than a mile. At lower speeds the range can be even greater.

When an organization has substantial off-net traffic, circuit switching offers a significant advantage over LANs. Access to external networks is an inherent part of the design of most circuit switches, but LANs can communicate with external networks only through gateway or bridge circuits. PBXs are designed to communicate over the telephone network, and many can be equipped with X.25 network interfaces. PBXs are also capable of being operated in tandem. With tandem switching local terminals can be connected to terminals in distant networks over tie lines, which are circuits that connect multiple PBXs together.

PBXs can often be used to advantage for data switching because the wiring is in place. Furthermore, users are familiar with the operation of a PBX and service technicians are trained in its maintenance, so that adding data capacity requires few changes to present operations.

Computer branch exchanges (CBXs) inherently have the capacity to collect statistics on voice and data usage for loading and administering the terminal efficiently. Most CBXs also have the ability to collect usage information for billing circuit costs back to the user. By contrast, most LAN applications lack accounting and billing features, and some lack the ability to gather usage statistics.

Despite their advantages, PBXs and other forms of circuit switches are not the universal solution to the data communications problems in many offices. Circuit switches have several limitations that outweigh their advantages in some applications. In the first place, they are expensive, and many organizations, particularly those where most of the telephone traffic is outside the organization, do not need a PBX. Rarely will any type of circuit switch be less expensive than a coaxial cable-based LAN.

Equally important, particularly in older systems, is the amount of time required to set up a connection. When terminals are engaged in extensive batch runs, setup time is only a small fraction of the total connect time and is relatively unimportant. For the bursty data traffic characteristic of the automated office, however, it often takes more time to establish a terminal-to-terminal connection than to send the traffic. Therefore, unless a circuit switch is designed for rapid access, it may limit throughput to an unacceptable degree.

Many devices also restrict throughput because of inherent limitations in the speed of data their circuits can handle. Unless the switch has been designed for high-speed data, it supports maximum data rates up to 9,600 b/s, and may limit the speed to 4,800 b/s. Furthermore, older electromechanical switches are notorious generators of noise impulses and can create a high data error rate.

Reliability is poorer with circuit switches than with other types of networks because all data must pass through an active central element. If the switch fails, all processing halts until it is restored. The most reliable types of LAN contain no active units aside from the terminals themselves and are, therefore, less susceptible to catastrophic failure. Reliability can be improved in circuit switches by duplicating common elements such as processors.

A PBX AS THE LAN HUB

Except for old devices susceptible to noise, a PBX contains all the elements of a limited-distance data switching network. If a PBX is already in place, there is no simpler method of implementing a local network, particularly for a small number of terminals. On the other hand, if the PBX is not in existence, few organizations will be able to justify adding one on the basis of a data switching requirement. An organization considering the installation of a new PBX, either as a replacement for an existing system or to fulfill a new voice-switching application, should consider its data transmission requirements and determine whether to acquire a dual purpose system. To aid in understanding how PBXs are used in switching both voice and data, it is necessary to review how PBXs are constructed and how the generations differ from one another.

AN OVERVIEW OF PBX TECHNOLOGY

A PBX consists of four elements (Figure 8.1). The *switching network* is a collection of electronic or electromechanical devices that connect circuits together. Until the late 1970s, the switching network was invariably electromechanical. Connections were made by the physical operation through space of a relay contact or crosspoint. Such networks, known as *space division networks,* had distinct limitations for data traffic. They were noisy, slow, and required maintenance to keep them in operating condition.

With the advent of digital electronics, the *time division network* evolved. In a CBX time division network, the incoming voice or data signal is sampled in the line **port** or in the station. Under control of the **central processing unit** a signal from one line port to another or to a **trunk** port is routed through the network. Data terminals can be connected to dedicated line ports, they can share ports with a telephone in an alternate voice-data arrangement, or the data and voice

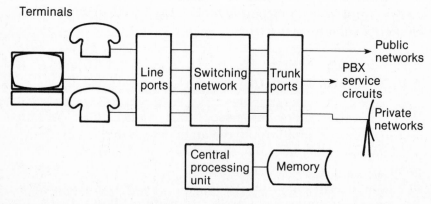

FIGURE 8.1   Block diagram of a PBX

signals can be multiplexed and applied to a combination voice/ data port. The alternate arrangement is the least expensive, but renders the telephone unusable during data transmission, and vice-versa.

To understand the operation of a PBX, let us follow the progress of a voice call through the major steps required in establishing a connection. A dialed-up data connection will be handled in exactly the same way.

Inside the PBX, a scanning circuit monitors lines and trunks to determine their state. When a station signals its intention to place a call, known as the *off-hook* state, the central control connects the line port to a specialized trunk port that delivers dial tone to the line. When the user begins to signal, say with a push button telephone, a circuit is attached to the line to receive the dialed digits. The central controller determines from the dialed digits whether the call is to be completed to another line port in the PBX or to an external trunk port. Ringing is applied to the appropriate port, and when the other station responds by answering (going off-hook), a connection is established. When the two stations complete the conversation, they are restored to an on-hook condition, and are ready for another call.

If the call goes off net to a long distance circuit, message accounting equipment registers the details of the call so the charges can be allocated to the originator. Also, while the call is in progress, the central controller collects statistical data that can be used to determine the grade of service the device is giving and to alert the system administrator of the need to add more capacity.

VOICE AND DATA PBX

In the past, PBXs were designed for voice communications alone and any data application was incidental. Today, many PBXs can integrate voice and data: A station user can talk over the telephone and use a data terminal simultaneously. Three methods of integrating voice and data are in use now.

Many voice/data PBXs use separate pairs of wire to connect the telephone to the voice port and the data terminal to the data port of a PBX. In many offices, spare wiring was provided when the PBX was installed which could be used to connect data terminals to the switch. Voice is usually transmitted in analog form and data in digital form without a modem. Data speeds up to 19.2 kb/s are common with this method.

Where spare cabling is not available, several data-over-voice carrier products are available to superimpose data over a voice signal. As shown in Figure 8.2, the voice signal is separated by filters from the data signal. Two analog carrier frequencies above the voice range provide a full-duplex data channel operating without a modem at speeds up to 19.2 kb/s. While such equipment is not inexpensive, it is often a less costly solution than installing new wiring.

The trend in current PBXs is to multiplex voice and data over a single high-speed circuit that is wired with one or two twisted-pairs to a single port in the PBX. With this method, the voice is digitized to a 64 kb/s signal at the terminal and integrated with a data signal at data rates also up to 64 kb/s. The two signals, together with signaling information, are transmitted at 128 kb/s or more to the PBX line port where the data and voice signals are separated and switched to their destinations. If a PBX has been designed for both voice and data, it can overcome some of the inherent disadvantages of a PBX in data switching.

PBX THROUGHPUT RESTRICTIONS

As we discussed in Chapter 5, a voice signal that is digitized results in a data signal of 64 kb/s. A PBX with a time division network using pulse code modulation can switch either a voice signal or a 64 kb/s data signal.

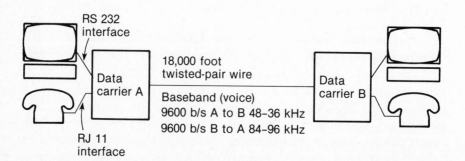

FIGURE 8.2   Data over voice carrier

Because human speech is inherently analog, a conversion from analog to digital and back to analog again must take place in each connection through a digital switch. This conversion either occurs in the terminal, as it does with some of the newer voice/data PBXs, or in the line port. If the conversion occurs in the terminal, the cost of the converter adds considerably to the cost of the station compared to the cost of an ordinary analog telephone set. For stations that need to transmit data, the cost is insignificant. As PBXs are intended primarily for voice communication, the analog-to-digital conversion in most machines occurs in the line port, but there is a growing trend toward digitizing the signal in the user's terminal.

Unless a PBX has been designed to accept direct digital inputs, the line ports are equipped only for analog, requiring the use of modems to convert the signal to analog before it is switched. Most PBXs built before the 1980s are equipped only with analog line ports and, therefore, can handle data only from modem-equipped terminals. The latest generation of switching systems provides digital line ports as well as analog ports. Some systems are designed for full 64 kb/s access, while others accept data only at lower speeds such as 19.2 kb/s.

PBX LOADING LIMITATIONS

If you plan to use a PBX for data transmission, you must be aware of the overload danger. The major variables affecting switching capacity are the **holding time** of each call, and the number of **attempts** from each terminal. The number of attempts is always higher than the number of completed calls because many calls fail to complete when the distant party is busy or does not answer. Also, many PBX features, such as third party conferencing and call transfer, generate additional attempts.

In evaluating the capacity of a PBX, it is important to determine its limiting factor. Usually, the number of attempts has the greatest effect on the processor, while the holding time has the greatest effect on the switch network. Many digital PBXs are designed with a nonblocking switch network, but calls can still be limited by the quantity of traffic sensitive circuits such as tone dialing receivers and trunk circuits.

A further limitation occurs because of the nature of voice and data traffic. The usage and holding time of voice traffic falls into a predictable pattern (see Figure 8.3). Data traffic, on the other hand, flows in a pattern almost diametrically opposed to voice. Some data terminals place only a small number of attempts per day, but once they establish a connection, they hold onto it for several hours. Batch processes are typical of this pattern. Other terminals, such as those of the automated office, place many attempts per day, but hold the connection for only a short time. For example, you can send a one-page, 300-word message over a 64 kb/s line in less than a second.

Adding data traffic to a PBX, therefore, can overload the switching network if the connections are of long duration; placing many short duration calls can overload the processor. A system designed to support both voice and data traffic avoids such danger, providing the information used to size it was accurate, and providing the traffic characteristics do not change. Each time a new data application is planned, or when significant changes are made in existing applications, close attention must be given to its effect on the PBX.

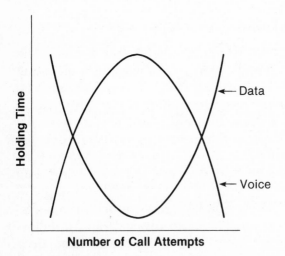

FIGURE 8.3 Holding time distribution of voice and data traffic

CALL SETUP TIME

As mentioned earlier, with an ordinary dialed-up connection, the time of establishing the connection can be significant compared to the time it takes to send a short data message. This is of minor concern with voice traffic and long batch runs from a computer, but it can significantly impede the operation of the automated office. Therefore, if a PBX is being considered for an automated office application, the call setup time should be evaluated.

OFF-NET COMMUNICATION

Off-net communication is inherent in the design of all PBXs. The gateway to external networks is through a trunk port. The protocols for communicating with a long-haul or metropolitan network through a telephone central office follow well-established conventions—an advantage of using a PBX as part of a data network.

PBXs with digital ports can be equipped with a shared modem pool for off-net communications. However, off-net communications over the switched telephone network are limited to 4800 b/s speeds. If the PBX is properly equipped, it can be directly interfaced to packet switched data networks. Usually, such networks require X.25 compatibility. The PBX must be certified compatible by the carrier.

PBX SELECTION CRITERIA

To summarize this discussion, an organization should consider using a PBX to integrate a local data network when one or more of the following conditions exist:

- A PBX with sufficient capacity is available.
- The organization has considerable off-net data traffic.
- The duration of data connections is long.
- The office is already wired with twisted-pair cable.
- Initial data requirements are small.

- Data speeds are 4800 b/s or less.
- A new PBX must be procured for other reasons.

An organization that has a PBX with sufficient capacity will find it a convenient way of implementing a local network, particularly for those networks that start small and gradually grow. Offsetting the advantages of a PBX in many organizations is its high cost. Despite the cost, if the system is already in place or if a new PBX must be added for voice traffic, an integrated voice/data PBX is an attractive alternative for many organizations.

If a new system is being considered, the following are important factors to consider when evaluating a PBX for use as a local data network.

1. Voice and data should be integrated as part of the system design, not as an add-on arrangement.
2. The system should be capable of integrating terminals from multiple vendors, including a full range of terminals that provide both telephone and data features.
3. The system should provide a gateway to common carrier networks, including both voice and packet-switched networks. The X.25 protocols should be available for connecting to public data networks.
4. The system should provide modemless operation within the local area and a modem pool for communication over the telephone network.
5. The system should provide the capability for both synchronous and asynchronous data communications. It may be important for the system to emulate an IBM 3270 terminal.
6. System design should provide easy access to shared peripheral equipment such as printers, computer output microfilm, optical character readers, and other such devices.
7. The system should include a redundant processor configuration and a nonblocking switching network. Shared circuits should be provided liberally enough that blockage is rarely encountered.
8. The system should be capable of linking LANs to the outside world through a gateway included in the PBX.

DATA SWITCHES

A data switch can be conceived as a specialized kind of PBX. In fact, the distinction between the two is becoming increasingly blurred as dual purpose systems come on the market. Although a PBX can serve dual functions, a data switch is a single purpose system that is capable of handling little, if any, voice traffic. Unlike most PBXs that pass data traffic through their ports, the data switch is in direct communication with the terminal, and therefore must be capable of supporting the protocols used by the terminal.

Other differences are in the external interfaces of the two types of systems. Data switch ports interface a recognized physical standard such as RS 232-C or X.21. By contrast, the PBX ports normally interface a two-wire cable pair. Most data switches are capable of interfacing a cable pair only through a modem. The signaling functions of a PBX line port are not required in a data switch. Instead, signaling takes place through the RS 232-C interface by a user-assigned code that is translated into the proper output port by the switch.

The type of interface is important to the organization applying a data switch because of lead length limitations. When the limitation of the interface is exceeded, either modems or line drivers are required to extend the cabling. RS 232-C is normally limited to 50 feet, but with special cable the distance can be extended to about 150 feet. RS 449 interfaces can be extended to 4,000 feet. It is most desirable to avoid the use of modems and line drivers because when large numbers of terminals are assigned, this can add significantly to the cost of the switch.

A dedicated data switch is capable of switching multiple terminals to a limited number of computer ports on a port contention basis. That is, if the ports are all busy, the switch queues the contending ports, or as it is sometimes called, puts the ports into a *camp-on* state, that is, waiting for a port to become available.

The gateway techniques of a data switch should also concern the user. The switch should be able to interface to the protocols of long-haul networks, such as the DDD (direct distance dialing) network. Depending on the application, an interface to an X.25 packet switched network may be required. If X.25 interface is important in your application, you should be certain the manufacturer warrants the switch certified for the X.25 protocol of the data network you plan to interface.

The ability of the switch to adjust to the transmitting speed of the terminal is also an important consideration. If the ports are fixed speed, a different access arrangement is required for each speed. For example, on dialed-up ports, different telephone numbers must be assigned for each range of speeds. A more flexible system is to have a port capable of automatically adjusting to the speed of the terminal.

Like any other switching device, a data switch has a limited amount of throughput capacity. An important distinction should be made between a switch and a contention network. With a contention network, terminals are attached continuously, and if they are sending no data, they impose no load on the network. With a switched network, when two ports are connected, a time slot is reserved for them, and they use network capacity whether data is being sent or not. Therefore, while contention networks are sensitive to traffic quantity, switched networks are sensitive to connect time. A well designed data switch should protect itself by disconnecting terminals that remain idle for a predetermined amount of time.

DATA SWITCH APPLICATIONS

If an existing PBX is unsuitable for data transmission because of limited size or obsolete technology, adding a data switch or a cable based LAN will often be less costly than adding a new PBX. With a separate data network, the data load can be isolated from the voice load and managed separately without the danger of overloading the voice network. However, adding a data switch in an existing building can require a costly rewiring job.

These are some factors that tend to make a data switch attractive:

- Off-net traffic requirements
- High-speed access between terminals
- Large bulk or batch traffic requirements
- Inadequate existing PBX for growing data traffic

- Switch capability to support required protocols
- Incompatible terminals with a bridge requirement

TIME-SHARED COMPUTER AS A LAN SWITCH

A time-shared computer can switch data through its access ports, but it differs from a data switch in several ways.
For one thing, it will not be equipped with a switching network. Instead, the computer reads data into its memory and
transmits it on an output port. It is therefore most efficient
when it is communicating with one of its attached terminals,
and less efficient in terminal-to-terminal communication.

A time-shared computer can be programmed for polling—
much like a circuit-switching function that dedicates a circuit
to message exchange between the host and the terminal.
Figure 8.4 shows multiple terminals connected to a single port
on the computer: In a predetermined pattern, the computer
sends a polling message to each terminal to see if it has data to
send; if it does, the terminal is given sole access to the port and
time long enough to send a message.

Polling is an inefficient technique for a local area network.
It is not adaptable to the frequent, short messages typical of
the automated office. Its primary application is to retrieve
data from distant terminals where conserving circuit costs is
more important than it is in a local network.

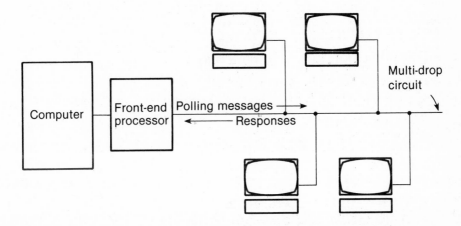

FIGURE 8.4   Polling on a data network

SUMMARY

After our brief look at circuit switching and packet switching in this and the last chapter, their applications in the local network can be better understood. When messages are long, circuit switching will win the nod over packet switching. For short, bursty traffic, a packet network will be more efficient. The cost of circuit switching is now somewhat lower than packet switching, but as the demand for packet switching grows, the potential for cost reduction is greater.

Circuit switching is more adaptable to voice transmission than packet switching because of the longer holding time of voice calls and the problem of packet loss and arrival out of sequence. Therefore, in an integrated voice and data network, circuit switching is usually the most economical mode. Designed in a star network configuration, it can make use of existing telephone cabling by connection to spare wire or by use of a short-range data-over-voice carrier.

Circuit switching presents no danger of messages arriving out of sequence, although this problem is not severe in local networks. By using spare voice ports for a limited number of terminals, circuit-switching data networks can often be established in a short time in organizations that already have a PBX.

Perhaps one of the greatest advantages of circuit switching is that most switches provide an easily accessible method of connecting to external networks. Connection to the long distance telephone network is an inherent feature of the PBX, and the gateway from circuit switches is less expensive than it is from many contention type networks. In the next chapter we will look at some typical circuit switches to understand their application in a local data network.

9

Circuit-switched Local Networks: Three Examples

As with other types of local networks, different kinds of circuit switches are available. In this chapter we will look at three systems that all belong to the circuit-switching category but are different in principle.

INTECOM IBX™

Although many circuit switches claim to handle simultaneous voice and data, the Intecom IBX is one of the few systems on the market that enables simultaneous voice and data transmission over two twisted-pair wires. Other systems multiplex data over voice with a data carrier system, or use separate wires and separate switching system ports for voice and data. The IBX allows both voice and data to pass simultaneously through the same port.

Figure 9.1 shows the architecture of the IBX. At the heart of the system is the Master Control Unit (MCU), a 32-bit redundant processor that provides overall system control and storage. Up to 32 Switching Network (SN) modules are connected to the MCU, providing a maximum of 8,192 paths through the network.

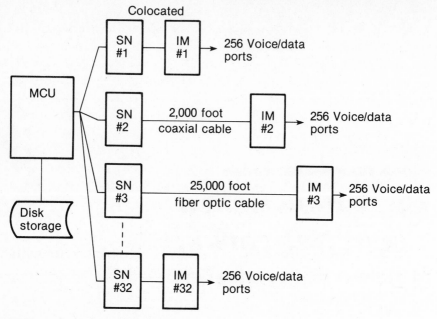

MCU   Master control unit

SN   Switching network

IM   Interface module

FIGURE 9.1   Architecture of Intecom IBX

The voice data ports are terminated in Interface Multiplexers (IM). As many as 32 IMs can be connected to the system. Each IM handles up to 256 voice data ports in four-port increments. The ports can be dedicated to analog voice, terminating up to 496 voice lines per IM, or to data, terminating as many as 512 data lines per IM. The microprocessor-equipped IMs can be remoted over coaxial cable up to 2,000 feet from the SN, or up to 25,000 feet over fiber optics. With this architecture the IBX can be distributed throughout a large building or over a wide area such as a college or industrial campus.

The ports support simultaneous voice/data transmission speeds up to 57.6 kb/s. Voice is digitized at the standard 64 kb/s rate that is used by pulse code modulation systems. Simultaneous voice and data transmission is made possible by merging voice and data bit streams to form a single digital-encoded signal. The IBX is also capable of transmitting packet-switched data to work stations in a burst mode at 10 mb/s.

Either standard analog or special electronic telephone instruments can be used in the IBX. The electronic telephone is known as Integrated Terminal Equipment (ITE), a device that digitizes voice, and optionally can accept input from data terminal equipment through standard RS 232-C or RS 449 interface connectors. ITEs are connected to the IM with two twisted-pair copper wires connected in a star topology. The ITEs are too expensive to substitute for ordinary telephone sets so the IBX is equipped to accept inputs from standard analog pushbutton dialing telephones where data communication is not required.

The centralized portions of the IBX can be backed up with emergency battery power for operation during power failures. Without battery backup the IMs, the ITEs, and any data terminals will be inoperative during a power outage. The system is equipped with a redundant processor. If the processor fails, the standby processor will continue without loss of calls or data transmission in progress. Battery backup and processor redundancy provide a high degree of reliability.

Intecom offers interface circuits called InteNet™ Packet Controllers for communications between the IBX and external network and between noncompatible data devices within the local network. For example, a word processor interface enables Wang, Lanier, and IBM word processors to communicate with one another, to share files, and to share common peripheral equipment.

Another interface, the X.25 IPC, allows communication between the IBX and external public packet networks such as Telenet and Tymnet. Communication with Ethernet LANs is made possible by the LANmark™ Ethernet, a system that links the IBX network with external coaxial networks or to Ethernet-compatible terminal equipment through the ITE.

The 3270 IPC allows asynchronous ASCII terminals to communicate with host computers using IBM 3270 application programs. The 3270 IPC communicates with the processor in bisynchronous format at speeds up to 9600 b/s.

The IBX S/10 can support a voice/data system with a minimum 256-port configuration, and the IBX S/80 can support a maximum 8,192-port configuration. InteCom claims that while all stations are engaged in voice or data transmission, the switching network has enough capacity to avoid blocking or degradation.

The IBX provides other features commonly associated with a voice-switched PBX: least-cost routing to public network facilities, an on-line directory, and call detail recording to enable allocating costs to the users. The IBX also provides a shared modem pool when data calls require interface to an analog common carrier network.

INFOTRON IS4000 INTELLIGENT SWITCHING SYSTEM

The Infotron IS4000 is a circuit switch primarily designed for data; its voice switching capability is limited and only optionally available through a voice interface card.

The IS4000 consists of a central switch that can accommodate up to 4,000 terminals operating at speeds up to 19.2 kb/s. The switch accommodates up to 2,000 simultaneous connections. Terminals are wired directly to ports on the IS4000 switch or to slave logic assemblies (SLAs) that can be operated remotely from the central unit. SLAs can operate up to 500 feet from the central unit without repeaters and up to 2,000 feet with repeaters. With modems wired to the ports, the network is not range limited.

The central unit and the SLAs are configured in a ring topology. Terminals are wired to the SLAs or directly to the IS4000 in a star topology. Figure 9.2 shows the system distributed throughout a building or campus. Ports can be assigned to dial-up lines from a PBX or to common carrier facilities for access outside the network.

Users on dedicated IS4000 ports address one another through user-assigned address codes that are converted to the appropriate port number. Users can also access a group of multiple ports assigned to a computer. If ports are all busy, the user can camp-on, waiting for an idle port. When a port becomes idle, the system selects the highest priority terminal from queue, and connects the terminal to the port.

The IS4000 system is able to adjust automatically to the data rate of an incoming signal over a dial-up port. It also has the ability to prompt users with locally defined messages.

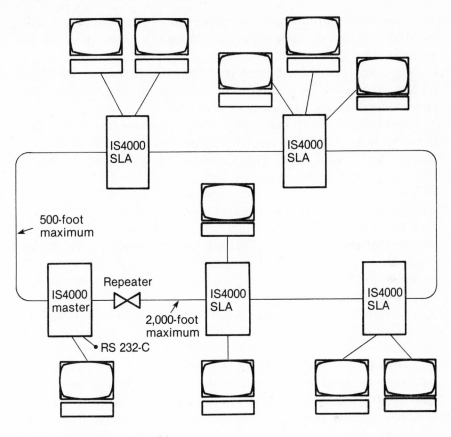

SLA   Slave logic assembly

FIGURE 9.2   Infotron IS4000 intelligent switching system

Messages can also be created locally to inform users of the operational status of the system, or to pass on bulletins and other messages.

ROLM CBX II™

In 1983, the ROLM Corporation introduced the CBX II as a successor to its popular CBX. The CBX II, which includes many enhancements over its predecessor, supports up to 10,000 users from multiple nodes. From one to fifteen nodes can be interconnected over short distances with coaxial cable, or can be located as far apart as 20,000 feet with fiber optic links.

Users are connected to ports at the node with single-pair wiring that accommodates simultaneous voice/data applications. The terminal-to-port connection can be up to 3,000 feet long and carries a data rate of 256 kb/s. Of this bandwidth, 64 kb/s are used for voice, 64 kb/s for data, and 128 kb/s for control and future expansion.

The CBX II is offered with a family of desktop terminals that can support either individual or simultaneous transmission of voice and data. The Cypress™ is a full-featured terminal providing both data and telephone communication. Alternately, the system can be equipped with ROLMphones in three models. Figure 9.3 provides a picture of the ROLMphone 120. Its more complex counterparts, the ROLMphone 240 and ROLMphone 400, provide additional telephone features. All instruments can optionally be equipped with a data communications module that can accept input from a data terminal or personal computer.

A unique feature of the CBX II is its ability to accept data at much higher rates than the 64 kb/s speed of the plug-in data port in the telephone terminals. Each node is equipped with a high-speed bus. The standard ROLMbus 74™ has a maximum 74 mb/s capacity, which is divided into 192 bidirectional channels, each rated at 192 kb/s. The optional ROLMbus 295 has a maximum 295 mb/s bus capacity, which can support 768 channels. The channels can be linked to carry higher speed data through a technique ROLM calls *dynamically allocatable bandwidth*. For example, six 192 kb/s channels can be linked to carry data up to 1.15 mb/s.

The CBX II can be equipped with X.25 interfaces at 56 kb/s or 9600 b/s for connection to public networks such as Tymnet, Telenet, and AT&T's Net 1000. The system can also be linked to LANs through bridge circuits and can be used as a gateway between an Ethernet LAN and public data networks or the public telephone network.

The CBX II provides a large organization with a processor-controlled circuit-switched environment complete with bridges and gateways that can integrate its voice and data communications requirements. Although the CBX II is not intended as a substitute for LAN, an organization's complete data communication requirements can be handled over a CBX II without limiting terminal-to-terminal throughput.

FIGURE 9.3   The ROLMphone 120

Photograph courtesy of the ROLM Corporation, used by permission.

10

Contention Networks

In a contention network, the terminals vie with one another for access. Citizen's band radio is a good example of a contention network. If users want to contact someone who is tuned to a channel, they wait until the channel is idle before they begin to transmit. Occasionally, two people begin to send at the same time, resulting in a garbled message. Simultaneous user access to the network results in a **collision,** and one user must agree to **back-off** while the other proceeds to send.

If traffic is light, a contention system is an efficient way of allocating the network's resources. Furthermore, configuration can be simple, for it requires no central controller. However, under heavy traffic conditions, the likelihood of frequent collisions increases. At peak capacity service begins to deteriorate as the network becomes consumed in collision recovery. Anyone who has contended for a busy CB channel has experienced the resulting chaos.

While an undisciplined contention system can be acceptable for voice communications, particularly in a hobbyist application, it is unsatisfactory for data communications where reliability is important. When data transmissions collide a portion of a packet is garbled. A contention network, therefore, requires some form of discipline to ensure maximum traffic support on a network.

PRINCIPLES OF CONTENTION NETWORKS

Figure 6.1 illustrates a simple contention network. Terminals connect to the network through media access controllers (MACs) that perform the following functions:

- Listen for incoming messages to terminals
- Assemble transmitted data into packets and disassemble received packets.
- Check for errors.
- Provide a buffer to accommodate terminal speed to that of the network.
- Monitor the busy/idle status of the network
- Provide recovery from collisions

The purpose of media access control is to create a circuit between the transmitting and receiving terminals so that the process of network sharing is completely transparent to the user. An early application of the contention method of allocating network access will illustrate its principle.

THE ALOHA SYSTEM

The University of Hawaii's Aloha network was put into operation in the early 1970s and became a prototype for later developments in contention-based access. The Aloha network linked terminals from seven campuses based on four islands. The central computer was on Oahu. Although the Aloha example is much too extensive a network to be classed as a local area network today, a brief outline of its operation will illustrate how a multi-access contention system works and demonstrate the problems such a network can encounter.

The system used UHF radio that could be heard by receivers at the central location. One frequency was used for the outlying terminals to transmit to the central computer, and a second frequency for the computer to send outbound traffic and messages acknowledging receipt of traffic. While the terminals could communicate with the central computer, they could not communicate with one another. Terminals contended for access to the inbound channel. Outbound traffic was broadcast to all sites so that a terminal could intercept the packets addressed to it.

Stations were free to transmit packets at random. Consequently collisions were frequent and considerable retransmission was required. If a station did not receive an acknowledgement message, it assumed a collision had occurred and retransmitted the packet. If any portion of a packet overlapped with another station's transmission, both packets were destroyed and had to be retransmitted.

This lack of control had many drawbacks. Some drawbacks were cured by a modified version called *slotted Aloha*. By this method, the packet lengths are fixed and the transmission time is divided into discrete intervals. A station can transmit only at the start of an interval. Therefore, a packet cannot be mutilated when one station starts to transmit in the middle of another station's interval.

BUS CONTENTION NETWORKS

A shortcoming of a radio-based packet network such as the Aloha system is the inability of terminals to hear one another. Because they cannot detect when the network is busy, terminals transmit at random, resulting in frequent collisions and wasted transmission time. When a contention network is implemented on a physical medium such as coaxial or fiber optics cable, the terminals are able to hear one another and refrain from transmitting on an occupied network. It is also unnecessary to restrict terminals to sending only to a central location. All terminals are capable of communicating with one another, although some can be restricted from direct communication for other reasons.

In contention networks, packets are broadcast to all terminals simultaneously, but only the addressee processes the message. The remaining MACs, recognizing the message is not intended for one of their terminals, discard it. When a terminal has traffic to send, it transmits its data to the MAC. (In some systems the MAC is packaged in a printed circuit board that plugs directly into the terminal's bus.) The MAC buffers the traffic, assembles it into packets, and listens for an idle period on the network. When the network is idle, MAC attempts to access the network by first sending a pulse and then monitoring it to see whether it is being distorted by a collision. If it has not collided with another station, the terminal has gained access to the network and is free to transmit a packet.

In an ideal network, packets would be neatly spaced in time intervals. If the inputs were perfectly controlled, the full capacity of the network could be utilized. Contention networks lack central control, however, and as traffic arrives in random spurts rather than in a controlled sequence, the stations must be disciplined to send their traffic in an orderly manner. The network discipline is built into the protocol in the MAC.

The MAC must determine when the network is idle and when a collision has occurred. One strategy for detecting collisions is through unmatched cyclical redundancy check (CRC) sums. This technique wastes network time because colliding packets must be retransmitted in their entirety. A more efficient method is to designate an interval for collision detection. A station wishing to acquire the network transmits a pulse during this interval and monitors it for distortion. If stations collide, both back off for a randomly selected interval and attempt to retransmit. If no collision occurs, the station assumes it has acquired the network and transmits a packet.

REASONS FOR LAN DISTANCE LIMITATIONS

This collision detection period is the principal reason that contention networks are restricted in diameter. To illustrate, assume that two terminals are located at opposite ends of a network with a diameter of one mile. Electrical pulses flow over coaxial cable about three-quarters the speed of light. If a station determines that the network is idle, there is a small but finite period in which the station is blinded to the possibility that another terminal has sent a pulse on the network. This interval, known as the *collision window*, is the length of time it takes a pulse to travel from the sending terminal to the furthest terminals on the network. Figure 10.1 illustrates the effects of two network nodes beginning to transmit at once.

In one kilometer of coaxial cable the collision window duration is approximately five microseconds. Most collisions are detected in a shorter time: When any node detects a collision, it transmits a jamming signal, and when the colliding nodes detect the jamming signal they back off. As stations transmit an acquisition pulse only during the contention interval, if that pulse is not distorted the station has acquired the network, and it is free to transmit a packet.

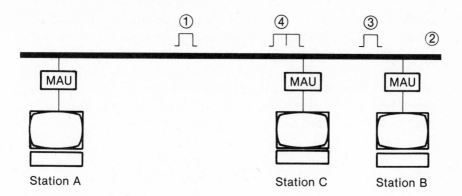

1. Station A transmits a pulse.
2. Station B listens to network after A transmits but before pulse from A arrives.
3. Hearing no data on network, B transmits a pulse.
4. Pulses collide.
5. Station C detects collision and transmits jamming signal.
6. Both A and B cease transmitting, then wait a random time before retransmitting.

FIGURE 10.1   Collision detection on a contention network

This system is known as **Carrier Sense Multiple Access with Collision Detection** (CSMA/CD). Carrier sense means the station listens to the network for the presence of a carrier before sending. Multiple access means the network is shared by several users. Collision detection occurs when a station transmits a pulse during the contention interval and listens to see if a collision has occurred.

CSMA can be further classified as persistent and nonpersistent, slotted and unslotted. In a persistent system, nodes involved in a collision attempt to resend damaged packets when the channel becomes idle again. However, the re-try interval must be randomly selected; if it is not, collisions can recur repeatedly between the same two nodes.

The probability of collision immediately after the transmission of a frame is high because several stations may have deferred their transmissions waiting for an idle period. Stations will seize the medium, collide, and then transmit at random intervals, which causes extra delays to the traffic. This situation can be eased with a nonpersistent system. When a collision occurs in a nonpersistent system, the station does not immediately try to resend the packet as the previous transmission ceases. Instead, it waits a random time after transmission before attempting access.

Slotted CSMA, like slotted Aloha, is a technique of allowing terminals to begin transmitting packets only at the start of a predefined time slot. The discipline imposed by slotting improves the network's efficiency.

CHARACTERISTICS OF A CONTENTION LAN

Although CSMA/CD is not ideal for every network application, it is an excellent method to use when the network is moderately loaded and the messages are short and bursty. Where messages are long, or where certain stations must have priority over others, noncontention systems or point-to-point networks are preferable. To aid you in deciding whether a contention system will fit your application, the advantages and disadvantages of contention networks are summarized below.

ADVANTAGES OF CONTENTION NETWORKS

The biggest advantage to a contention network is its simplicity of design. There are no central elements to fail. Each terminal stands on its own, isolated from the others. The total network will fail only if something happens to the transmission medium, or if a terminal malfunctions and sends a continuous stream of data (a streaming terminal).

Another advantage of a contention network is its high throughput rate compared to circuit switching. A contention network is not limited to the speeds imposed by networks with voice frequency bandwidths. Although the network itself does not limit transmission speed, the speed can be limited by the interface between the MAC and the terminal. Also, the network must place some limitations on each station to avoid the danger of a prolonged one-station access to the network, blocking entry for contenders. If the load is light, a contention network should be able to handle a continuous stream of high-speed traffic between two terminals.

Terminals can easily be added to contention networks. As each terminal stands independently, a terminal is connected to a controller that is coded to the appropriate address. A further advantage is that unlike circuit-switched terminals that use network capacity for the duration of the sessions, terminals on contention networks use capacity only when they are sending data.

DISADVANTAGES OF CONTENTION NETWORKS

The limitation of a contention network is best explained by the concept of peak-to-average load. This ratio would be one to one if a network never experienced peaks, that is, if the load was perfectly uniform throughout the day. For most organizations, this is far from the actual situation. Most networks experience busy hours of the day, busy days of the week, and busy seasons of the year.

These busy peaks are difficult to predict in a new application because they depend on the nature of the organization itself. For example, an office supporting a department store complex would undoubtedly have seasonal peaks around Christmas, daily peaks on Friday in preparation for a busy weekend, and occasional hourly peaks at the 9:00 or 10:00 A.M. opening as the initial rush begins. A large travel agency, on the other hand, might have a seasonal peak in March and April as tourists begin preparing for their summer vacations. Probably, they experience daily peaks on Monday morning after clients have spent a weekend planning trips.

In some organizations peak traffic in an eight-hour work day can be three or four times greater than average. In shorter time segments, the ratio might be even higher. For example, if a large part of the organization takes a break from 10:00 to 10:15, and checks its electronic mail boxes on return, the momentary load could be high.

Most networks exhibit a response time curve similar to that shown in Figure 2.5. When the load is light, response time is excellent. As the load increases, the network impedes the response time until at some point the curve turns sharply upward. In evaluating a contention network you should inquire how the manufacturer rates the capacity of the network and at what load the knee of the curve is breached. In a contention network, although the data transfer rate between terminal servers can be high, say 5 or 10 mb/s, the capacity of the network is much less than the theoretical maximum.

Network throughput is limited by several factors. Let us consider the data transfer rate of the network itself. If the transfer rate is 10 mb/s, this is the maximum the network can handle under the most ideal conditions. Any attempts to send beyond this rate will be blocked. Another limiting factor is the number of overhead bits that must be transmitted for each packet. Overhead bits are required by the protocol, but transmit no information. If asynchronous data is being sent, the start and stop bits also create overhead. If two terminals are communicating in an asynchronous mode, and if the network transmits the start and stop bits, the throughput of data will be reduced by about 20 percent (2 start-stop bits/10 total bits).

The time spent in collision recovery also limits the throughput. No contention network is immune from collisions, and when they occur, the recovery method reduces throughput. Some LANs that rely on the check-sum code to detect errors require retransmission of an entire packet when packets collide. Other networks detect collisions during the collision window, and are more efficient.

The ability of the protocol to use all the available time for data transmission is a limiting factor. To illustrate this point, consider the control system used to regulate entrance onto a congested expressway. When a freeway is almost empty of vehicles, any vehicle can move freely. For example, the 55 mph limit of an expressway might be comparable to the 10 mb/s speed of a contention bus network. Cars enter the freeway by accelerating down an entrance ramp until they reach the maximum speed and slide into a vacant space between adjacent vehicles. This self-regulation works well until the expressway becomes congested; then the cars' speed drops well below the highway limit. Vehicles entering from the on-ramps begin to choke the expressway, and the speed of traffic drops even lower.

To alleviate the situation, many expressways use on-ramp controls. Rather than allow any vehicle to enter at its own volition, traffic lights regulate the ramps. Although this causes queuing on the entrance ramps, the traffic along the main expressway (or bus) is allowed to proceed at a more orderly rate.

In a data network this queuing of traffic is known as *flow control*. The flow control process a LAN uses has an effect on the throughput. Likewise, packet length affects throughput because of the greater ratio of overhead bits to information bits per packet.

The major disadvantage of CSMA/CD is that as traffic increases the uncertainty of data delivery increases. The data rate, the packet size, and the cable length are all dependent on one another. One solution to this problem is token passing, which makes it possible to design a more predictable network (see Chapter 11).

A further limitation of CSMA/CD is the network diameter. Circuit-switched and point-to-point networks are essentially unlimited in the distance between terminals. With contention networks, as the diameter increases the throughput rate decreases because the collision window becomes wider to accommodate the longer transit time. For organizations confined to narrow geographical limits, the distance limitation becomes unimportant. For others, the limitation requires the use of repeaters or separate networks linked by gateways.

The broadcast nature of contention networks can create a security problem. Because every message appears on the input to every terminal, terminals can receive messages addressed to others merely by changing address. The use of encryption can preserve the integrity of messages, but for many applications it is undesirable to have even encoded information consistently accessible to other users.

Finally, off-net communications can be more expensive for contention networks than with other types. These networks require a special gateway server to convert from the contention network protocols to those of a long-haul common carrier.

NETWORK DESIGN

To design a contention network, you must understand both the capabilities of the network and the characteristics of your own traffic. For each terminal, you must determine the output speed and the amount of data transmitted. Determine the average amount of traffic per day, the peak amount per hour, which hours represent the peak, the busiest days of the week, and the busiest seasons of the year. Combine the traffic from all terminals and add an increment for overhead bits used by the protocol; anticipate future growth requirements.

Obtain from the LAN manufacturer the expected throughput of the network, given your traffic characteristics. If your peak traffic does not exceed the network capacity, delays should be acceptable. Wherever the peak exceeds capacity, you have the following choices:

- Tolerate the delay
- Shift the load
- Increase throughput by choosing another network
- Split the network into separate segments

Network design is beyond the scope of this book, but it is critical that the performance of a LAN be determined in advance of implementation either by use of an analytical model or by simulation. As we discuss in Chapter 16, a key factor in selecting a network will be your confidence in the vendor's ability to design it to your requirements.

NETWORK EFFICIENCY

You will discover a wide variety of claims concerning the efficiency of contention networks. Some sources have claimed the efficiency of CSMA/CD to be as high as 90 percent. However, it is generally agreed that contention networks handle no more than approximately 3 mb/s throughput on a network with a 10 mb/s data rate. Such claims seem contradictory, and to some degree they are. However, the industry lacks a standard means of measuring network efficiency, and therein lies the problem.

Let us postulate a definition of efficiency to illustrate the measurement dilemma. Assume that efficiency is the ratio of output/input. Network efficiency then might be stated:

$$\frac{\text{Maximum Data Throughput}}{\text{Data Rate on Bus}}$$

In a contention network if the data rate is 10 mb/s and the network is capable of handling a peak throughput of 8 mb/s, we could state the network efficiency to be 80 percent. But before we could make such a claim, we have to add qualifiers. The first difficulty is the lack of a standard data signal to approximate the real world in which LANs must perform. There is a great deal of difference, for example, between the efficiency that can be achieved with a network supporting many contenders and one that supports a single sender transmitting bulk data to a single receiver. Ignoring the fact that a contention network would be a poor choice for bulk data transfer, it would be possible to achieve a high degree of efficiency because no time would be lost in collision recovery or in waiting for access to a busy bus.

However, a network with many contenders sending short messages, many not long enough to occupy a full packet, would achieve a low throughput rate. To discuss efficiency, we must be prepared to discuss the character of the traffic and the number of contenders the network is required to handle.

Another question concerns the number of overhead bits the network is expected to handle and whether these are counted as actual data throughput. As far as the end user is concerned, these contribute nothing to the information being communicated; to be accurate they should be deducted from the total throughput rate. If you are sending asynchronous data, in addition to the protocol the start and stop bits also add overhead while contributing nothing to data throughput.

In bulk data transfer with no contenders where the network is invulnerable to failure, it would be possible to pack all the data into one extremely long packet and do away with all the overhead. In the real world, that is not practical, and packet length and error checking protocols have a great deal to do with network efficiency. Nevertheless, a vendor may include overhead bits to state network efficiency in terms of the effective data rate on the bus.

All these factors make the measurement of network efficiency an iffy proposition. The real measure of the network is the response time that results under the conditions your own traffic will impose. If the LAN has plenty of capacity to handle your traffic, blockage will not occur; if it is capacity-limited, the users will experience delays, and that is the factor you want to evaluate.

APPLICATIONS OF CONTENTION NETWORKS

Despite their limitations, contention networks have their place in many organizations. The typical organization purchasing a contention network is likely to have these characteristics:

- A range between outer terminals of one mile or less
- Traffic characteristics with a minimum of peak periods
- Security as an issue of secondary importance
- Most communication within the network
- Off-net communication of secondary importance
- A need to share common resources such as a data base or common peripherals with frequent random access by multiple terminals

In some applications, the contention network's lack of discipline can limit response time, and the simplicity of distributed control must be sacrificed for the greater efficiency of a more disciplined control system. In this case, a form other than a contention-based system is required.

THE IEEE 802.3 STANDARD

The 802.3 standard is a network access design similar to Xerox's Ethernet (discussed later in this chapter) and is intended for commercial or light industrial use. The 802.3 standard recommends a method of implementing the first and second ISO layers, as well as the physical and data link layers, for a contention network. The IEEE standard is not a complete network in itself: although the protocol is capable of detecting errors, it does not include an error recovery process.

Figure 10.2 shows the elements of 802.3. The ISO link layer is divided into two sub layers: the Link Layer Control (LLC) and the Media Access Control (MAC). Together the LLC and MAC correspond to the ISO data link layer. The layers in the 802.3 standard interact with higher layers for error recovery procedures and network control functions. The interface between the media access sublayer and the LLC transmits and receives frames and provides status information to forward to higher levels of error recovery. The interface between the media access and the physical layers includes signals for framing, detecting, collision recovery, and serial bit-streams passing between the two layers.

OVERVIEW OF THE NETWORK

The 802.3 network is composed of cable segments of a maximum 500 meters (1,640 feet) long—the greatest distance that can be spanned at the maximum signaling rate of 20 mb/s. Figure 10.3 shows as many as five segments interconnected through a maximum of four repeaters. The repeaters sense carriers from both cables. When the repeater detects a carrier

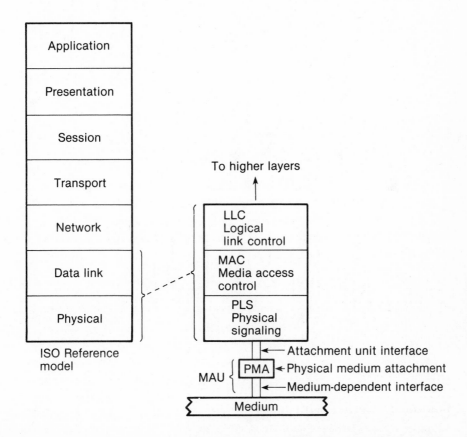

FIGURE 10.2   IEEE 802.3 CSMA/CD LAN

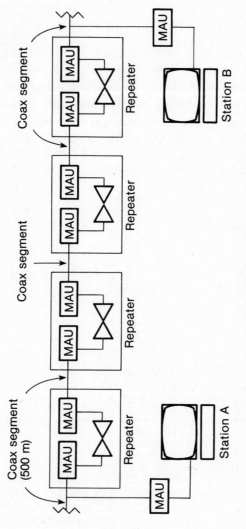

FIGURE 10.3   IEEE 802.3 maximum configuration

from one cable segment, it repeats the signal to the other cable segment.

The repeaters also perform the collision detection and avoidance functions that the media access sublayer performs for the terminals. If a repeater detects a collision within the transmission segment, it sends a jamming signal to each of the segments. Each cable segment can handle a maximum of 100 Medium Attachment Units spaced a minimum of 2.5 meters apart.

MEDIUM ACCESS UNIT (MAU)

By design the **MAU** is as simple a device as possible. (It is the MAC that assumes the majority of the control functions.) The MAU consists of a physical connector that bridges on the transmission medium with an impedance high enough to avoid discontinuities in cable impedance.

The physical attachment interface specification supports MAUs for baseband coaxial cable, broadband coaxial cable, and baseband fiber. With coaxial cables it is important that the cable be grounded in only one place in the network. This requires that all connectors be insulated to prevent them from being inadvertently grounded.

MEDIA ACCESS CONTROL (MAC)

The media access sublayer consists of two elements, the Physical Link Signaling (PLS) and the Media Access Control (MAC). The media access sublayer has two major functions. The IEEE committee calls the first function *data encapsulation.* This comprises framing and synchronization, addressing, and error detection. The IEEE assigns the second function, *medium access management,* to collision avoidance and recovery. The function of the PLS is to convert incoming data bits to Manchester code and then offer them to the MAU for transmission. With Manchester code each bit cell is divided into two complementary halves. In the center of the bit cell, the coding undergoes a transition as shown in Figure 10.4. A positive transition forms a binary one, and a negative transition, a zero.

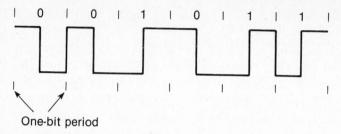

One-bit period

FIGURE 10.4   Manchester coding

THE CSMA/CD FRAME

Figure 10.5 shows the composition of the frame used in the 802.3 standard. The first block, the preamble, is transmitted to allow the physical signalling components of the MAC to reach a steady state. This is followed by a one-octet (byte) block of a set pattern that identifies the start of a frame.

The next two blocks contain the destination and source addresses. These blocks can be either two or six octets long—the length of the block is left up to the manufacturer. In the 48-bit block, 46 bits are available for the address; in the 16-bit block 15 bits are available for the address. This allows as many as 2^{46} bits for addressing, which seem like an impossibly large number of addresses for a single network. The intention is to provide worldwide addressing without requiring translation. Addresses can be assigned to individual stations, groups of stations that are logically related, or broadcast to all stations on the network.

Following the address blocks is a two-octet block indicating the length of the data block. This is followed by the data block itself. If the required minimum length of the data block is not met, it is lengthened with a sub-block called a *pad*. Error checking is accomplished with a CRC block 32 bits long.

XEROX ETHERNET

The Xerox Ethernet system is a baseband contention network that uses CSMA/CD for access. The IEEE 802.3 standard was derived from Ethernet and closely parallels it, but is not identical in all respects. The differences are slight, however, and for all practical purposes Xerox's Ethernet can be considered to meet the 802.3 standard. Before the standard was approved, the developers of Ethernet provided its specification to any manufacturer paying a modest license fee. Therefore, it is available from multiple vendors, and many devices are available to interface computers and DTE to Ethernet.

The *ether,* once postulated as the medium through which radio waves traveled, lent its name to the medium that carries data signals in Ethernet. Ethernet is not medium dependent— it can be implemented over twisted-pair wire, coaxial cable, fiber optics, radio, or light beams.

Ethernet, which is illustrated in Figure 10.6 with the devices and services it supports, consists of the transmission medium and a medium attachment unit that consists of a transceiver and an Ethernet controller. In the versions offered by various vendors, the MAU is either contained in a unit, or the controllers and transceivers on the cable can be separated by as much as 50 feet.

The Ethernet specification does not cover a complete network. Instead, the specification covers the physical and data link layers of the OSI protocol. The physical layer is implemented through Ethernet transceivers that connect to the medium. A cable segment connects the transceivers to an Ethernet controller plugged into a computer's bus or connected to a serial port on a terminal. The remaining network layers must be provided in the terminals' software.

Although the link protocol in Ethernet provides CRC error checking, it is not designed to provide error-free data transport. If the application requires an error-free channel

Preamble	SFD	Destination address	Source address	L	Data block	Frame check sequence
7 octets	1 octet	2 or 6 octets	2 or 6 octets	2 octets	Length unspecified	4 octets

SFD   Start frame delimiter
L   Length

FIGURE 10.5   IEEE 802.3 frame format

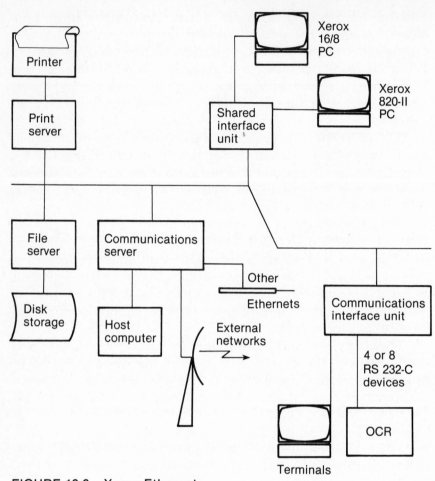

FIGURE 10.6   Xerox Ethernet

equipped with acknowledgement and retransmission at error detection, then a higher level protocol corresponding to those from the third to the seventh OSI layers must augment the basic Ethernet.

Figure 10.7 shows the format of an Ethernet frame. The destination address is a 48-bit sequence specifying the address of a single user on the network, a multi-cast group address of multiple stations, or a broadcast address for all stations on the network. The source address field contains the address of the transmitting station. The data field contains 46 to 1,500 data bytes, followed by a 32-bit frame check field that contains the CRC value for the data within the frame.

Ethernet operates at 10 mb/s and allows 500 meter spacing between repeaters with a total network diameter of 2500 meters. A maximum of 100 stations per segment are supported over the standard 50 ohm coaxial cable in a baseband mode. Signaling, collision detection, and other functions of the network are identical to the IEEE standard. Like 802.3, the Ethernet protocol consists of two layers corresponding to the physical and link layers. Xerox has developed network, transport, session and presentation layers to provide a fully operational network.

The major network components are the servers, controllers, transceivers, and the transmission system. The controller corresponds to the MAC and LLC of the 802 standard. The controller performs the functions of transmitting and receiving, signaling, data buffering, assembling and disassembling packets, recognizing addresses, and controlling the carrier sense and collision detection functions.

Ethernet uses the 6 octet addressing option of the 802.3 standard. Packets can be from 72 to 1,526 octets in length with a spacing of 9.6 microseconds between packets. The minimum packet length is required because any segment on the network shorter than the minimum packet size is discarded as a collision fragment.

In addition to the Xerox product, other Ethernet-compatible networks have been produced by companies such as Ungermann-Bass, InteCom, Ohio Scientific, and 3COM. Contention-based networks such as ConTel Information System's ConTelNet, Corvus' Omninet, Nestar Systems' Cluster One, and the Sytek LocalNet 20 use CSMA/CD, but are not compatible with the Ethernet protocols.

Preamble	Destination address	Source address	Type	Data field	CRC
8 octets	6 octets	6 octets	2 octets	46–1500 octets	4 octets

FIGURE 10.7 Ethernet frame format

SUMMARY

The primary problem with CSMA/CD is that it is statistically based. That is, the user has no assurance of being able to gain network access during heavy load periods. The solution proposed by other manufacturers is to use a *deterministic* network, one that offers access that can be predicted in advance and controlled. In the next chapter we will explore the alternatives for avoiding the unpredictability of CSMA/CD.

11

Noncontention Networks

The main advantage of contention networks is their simplicity and, therefore, low cost. However, in some applications the disadvantages outweigh the lower cost. When the network is congested or heavily loaded, throughput efficiency deteriorates. Moreover, the free-for-all access structure of CSMA/CD allows no way of predicting how long the delays for a given station will be. Aside from flow control at the network interface, high-priority traffic cannot be allocated network time to ensure preferential delivery.

Variations of CSMA/CD have introduced controls to the network by sacrificing simplicity. Two disparate forms of network are needed—one without control (CSMA/CD), and one with some form of central control. In this chapter we will look at control methods. While particular emphasis will be placed on token passing, we will first look at older control techniques that have supported data communications for the past few decades.

POLLING

Figure 8.4 shows a network configured for polling. Terminals are wired over a multidrop line to a terminal controller or front-end processor that interfaces the line to a host computer. To prevent all terminals from attempting to send at once, the terminal controller sends a polling message to each terminal, asking if it has traffic.

Polling is commonly handled on either a *roll-call* or a *hub polling* basis. With roll-call polling the controller sends a message to each station in turn. The message contains the station address, and each terminal responds only to its own address even though it receives all the polling messages. Terminals with high priority traffic can be polled more frequently than those at the lower end of the scale.

Roll-call polling over half-duplex lines requires two line reversals for each polling message—one when the controller sends, and one when the terminal sends. These line reversals consume circuit time, a problem that can be mitigated with hub polling. In this method the controller sends a polling message to the most distant terminal. If that terminal has traffic it sends it; otherwise it passes the polling message to the next terminal toward the controller. The polling message is passed toward the host until a terminal is found with traffic to send. In this manner circuit time spent in reversals is saved.

Polling is a reasonably efficient method for a host to collect data from remote terminals, but it is inefficient for terminal-to-terminal communication. Two techniques can be employed to handle communication between terminals. One technique is for the host to collect the message from one terminal and resend it to another terminal. This method uses twice as much network time as the alternative technique, which is direct terminal-to-terminal communication. The problem with direct terminal communication is that end-to-end error checking will be lost unless the terminals are smart enough to perform error checking in either a master or slave configuration.

Another drawback to polling is the consumption of circuit time in sending polling messages only to receive a negative response when a terminal(s) has no traffic to send. Furthermore, adding or removing a network terminal requires reprogramming of the host. The seriousness of this problem depends on the vendor's technique for handling and authenticating changes to the network. Finally, network security is poor with a polling system because terminal-to-host traffic is broadcast on the network for all terminals to hear.

Polling networks are expensive to implement. Although the circuit costs are low, any saving in circuit costs can rapidly be offset by costs of the host system. Therefore, polling is of limited usefulness in the short distance requirements of local area networks. It is more attuned to long-haul networks where circuit savings can offset the price of the host. Also, as with any network having central control, polled networks are susceptible to failure. Any time the host is down, the entire network is down unless some provisions have been made for direct terminal-to-terminal communication.

CIRCUIT SWITCHING

Circuit switching is covered in detail in Chapters 8 and 9 and will not be repeated here, except to indicate that circuit switching is a form of noncontention network. Like polling, circuit switching uses central control to allocate network capacity.

TOKEN PASSING

Many of the disadvantages of central network control can be overcome by distributing control to the stations or nodes. Token passing is a widely applied form. A **token** is a configuration of bits that circulate through the network in a predetermined pattern. A station transmits only after acquiring the token. Therefore, a token passing network is deterministic—that is, its traffic capacity is predictable and stations do not interfere with one another when attempting to send traffic. Ring and bus topologies predominate in token networks.

In a ring network, the token passes in sequence between stations. A token in a ring network is like a train with an empty boxcar. The car is loaded with data by the station that acquires it. If a station has traffic to send, acquiring the token allows it to access the network long enough to send one or more frames of data. After the data is sent, the station reinserts the token on the network where it is received by the next station. If that node has no traffic to send, it passes the token forward. Traffic always flows in a single direction in the ring. Each node receives a communication from one neighbor and passes it on to the next.

A token ring net has two basic rules. First, a node cannot put a message on the network unless it has the token. This permits only one node to transmit at a time. Second, only the node that puts the message on the network can remove it. If the receiving node has been bypassed, the sending node recognizes that the message has not been delivered because when the message returns, it contains no acknowledgement.

In a bus topology, messages and the token are broadcast to all stations simultaneously. The token can be circulated in any sequence as opposed to the series sequence required by the ring network. To do so, however, requires either that the token contain the routing sequence, or that each node know the identity of the stations immediately preceeding and following it. This reduces the flexibility of the network: to add or rearrange stations requires that each node be programmed with the new routing algorithm. This is clarified through our discussion on the IEEE standard 802.4 network in a later section.

Unlike polling, with its continuous transmission of polling messages and receipt of responses from each station, token passing uses a minimum amount of time for network control. Stations are programmed not to interfere with one another because only the station with the token is permitted to send.

In contrast to CSMA/CD in which the stations experience progressively increasing amounts of delay as the load increases, token passing distributes a share of capacity equally among all stations and queues traffic outside the network. In this way access delay can be calculated with a reasonable degree of accuracy.

Because there is no requirement to listen for collisions, a token-passing network is not limited by the transit time as is the case with CSMA/CD. Instead, the limiting factor in network length is the physical attenuation of the cable. A token bus, therefore, allows greater network diameter than with CSMA/CD. A token ring allows even greater network diameter because each data bit is repeated by each station.

Token passing is not without its disadvantages, however. The network is vulnerable to the loss or mutilation of a token, which can occur if a station fails at the time it possesses the token. Unlike CSMA/CD, in which stations can be added to the network without affecting other stations, with token passing the network must be initialized so that other stations recognize the addition or removal of a station. To accomplish the 802 committee's objective of making the network invulnerable to the failure of a single station, all stations must be equipped to handle the network control functions. In contrast to CSMA/CD where control is distributed to each station, with token passing, each station contains the elements of a central controller. Thus the protocols are more complex and expensive to implement.

CONTROL IN A TOKEN NETWORK

One reason for selecting a noncontention network is to gain more predictable response time. In a statistical network it is possible, although unlikely, for a terminal to be denied access to a busy network. In a deterministic network such as a token network, each terminal receives a proportionate share of time. However, if a token is lost because of a noise burst, power failure to the node possessing the token, or other such reason, the network cannot handle data until the token is recreated. If no carrier is sensed, the nodes begin timing, and when the timeout period is reached, the token is recreated by one terminal. The network protocol must determine which token will be reinserted because the problem of duplicate tokens is as severe as no token.

To prevent an interruption in data flow when a station fails, alternate or redundant paths can be provided, or each station can be equipped with a bypass feature to isolate itself if it malfunctions. Adding nodes can also result in physical disruption of the network. To avoid this, plan for additional node connections in advance and equip the cable with the circuitry to admit a new station.

One way of ensuring the health of the network is to designate one node as the network controller with the task of monitoring the circulating token and regenerating it if it is lost. The network controller, or supervisory node as it is sometimes called, has other functions including monitoring the network for unclaimed wandering packets and killing them after they have circulated a given amount of time. The controller in some networks monitors and maintains traffic statistics for loading and administrative purposes. In some networks the controller can change routing algorithms if terminals are added, removed, or their priority changed.

While token networks eliminate the collisions that limit throughput, they are more expensive and complicated to implement than contention networks. Although there are many different designs on the market, the IEEE 802.4 (token bus) and IEEE 802.5 (token ring) architectures will likely dominate in the future.

THE TOKEN BUS LAN IEEE 802.4

A token bus LAN uses the same basic topology as CSMA/CD, but control is similar to a token ring network. Although messages are broadcast to all stations in the network simultaneously, as with CSMA/CD, the stations are formed into a logical ring in which control is passed in sequence from station to station. Figure 11.1 shows the physical and logical topology of a token bus network. Each station is programmed with the address of its preceding and succeeding stations. When a station with no traffic to send receives the token, it passes the token to the succeeding station. If it does have traffic to send, it creates a frame of data and sends it on the network.

The token bus standard allows a wider physical diameter than a CSMA/CD bus. By selecting cable grade, the network can accommodate a length of from 1,280 meters (4,200 feet) to 7,600 meters (25,000 feet). Although the network diameter can be increased by repeaters, most LAN application ranges are sufficient without their use.

TOKEN BUS FRAME FORMAT

The token bus frame format is shown in Figure 11.2. The first block is a preamble of one to three octets, depending on the speed of the network. The next block is a start delimiter, which is one octet of a predetermined bit pattern. The frame control octet establishes the class of the frame. This is followed by two- or six-octet destination and source addresses. As with the CSMA/CD standard, addresses can be of three types, individual, group, or broadcast.

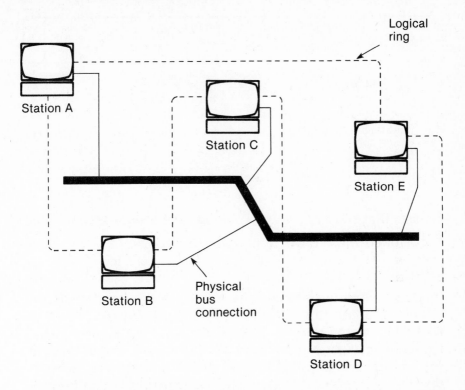

FIGURE 11.1   Physical connection and logical ring on an IEEE
802.4 token bus

Following the address is a data block, a four-octet error-
checking block, and a one-octet ending delimiter block. The
data block size is limited only by the requirement that 8,191 or
fewer octets are permitted between the start and end
delimiters.

MODULATION METHODS

The 802.4 standard recognizes three modulation methods.
The first type is a single-channel, frequency shift keyed (FSK)
network on a coaxial bus with a data rate of 1 mb/s. The second type is also FSK on coax at 5 or 10 mb/s. The third type is a
dual-channel broadband standard at 5 or 10 mb/s using headend equipment to separate the transmit and receive frequencies. The modulation techniques are similar to those discussed
in Chapter 13, Broadband Local Networks. You may wish to

Preamble	SD	FC	Destination address	Source address	Data unit	Frame check sequence	ED
1-3 octets	1 octet	1 octet	2 or 6 octets	2 or 6 octets	0 octet min. 8,191 octet max. between SD and ED	4 octets	1 octet

SD Start delimiter
FC Frame control
ED End delimiter

FIGURE 11.2 IEEE 802.4 token bus frame format

refer to that chapter for an explanation of broadband modulation techniques.

TRUNK COUPLING UNIT

Corresponding to the MAU in the 802.3 standard is the Trunk Coupling Unit (TCU) in a token bus network. In single frequency networks the TCU is a simple T coupler with a bridging unit that can be coupled to the Media Access Control. In the dual frequency network, the TCU is a more complex directional coupler that separates the transmitting and receiving frequencies and couples them to the Media Access Control.

MEDIA ACCESS CONTROL

The MAC in a token bus performs many of the same functions that it does in CSMA/CD, such as address recognition and frame encapsulation, but several functions are added to accomplish the more complex control required. The primary functions of the MAC are to determine when its station has the right to access the medium, to recognize the presence of a token on the bus, and to determine when and how to pass the token to the next station. Under control of its station management unit, the MAC must be capable of initializing or resetting the network. It must be able to recognize when a token has been lost, and to regenerate it when necessary. The addition of a new station to the network, or the recognition of when a succeeding station has failed must also be accomplished by the MAC.

The MAC is divided by the IEEE standard into machines, which will be briefly described here. The *interface machine* is the circuitry that connects the logical link control (LLC) to the MAC. It is responsible for receiving and generating the primitives used to communicate with the LLC. It performs the additional functions of queuing service requests and recognizing when incoming messages are intended for it.

The *access control machine* is the most complex of the elements in the MAC. It communicates with the interface machine and with the station management unit to accomplish such functions as token control, addition of new stations, fault detection and recovery, and control of access to the bus.

The *receive machine* assembles frames from the physical layer, recognizes frame start and end delimiters, and passes received data to the access control machine. A companion *transmit machine* accepts frames from the access control machine and transmits them to the physical layer, adding the start and end of frame delimiters. An optional *regenerative machine* is used in repeater stations.

TOKEN PASSING ON A TOKEN BUS

On the surface, token passing does not seem to be a complicated affair, and if all goes well, the protocol has little work to do. Each MAC is programmed with the address of its successor and predecessor stations. When it passes the token to its successor, it listens for the successor's transmission. If the transmission is received, it assumes that all is well. However, if the successor fails to transmit, the MAC begins to assess the state of the network. For example, assume that Station A in Figure 11.1 has sent a token to its successor, Station B, but B has failed and does not respond. Then A sends a second token and again listens for a response. Hearing no response, A assumes that B has failed and transmits a message asking which station follows B.

Each MAC on the network compares its predecessor station number with the number contained in the "who follows" message. C, the station that was B's successor, responds to the message. A substitutes C in its successor station address, and B is effectively bypassed.

Adding a new station to the network, or reinserting a

previously failed station requires equipping two of the stations on the network, the preceding and succeeding stations, with the address of the new station. This is accomplished during an interval known as the response window. During the response window, a station can bid for a place on the network. If two or more stations do not bid simultaneously, the new station is added gracefully. If collision occurs during the response window, a recovery procedure is required which further complicates the protocol. The response pattern can also be revised by reinitializing the network.

THE TOKEN RING LAN, IEEE 802.5

The token ring, illustrated in Figure 11.3, is both a logical and a topological ring. Each station in a token ring is a repeater, thus enabling wider physical range than that possible with bus networks. However, this is achieved at the price of greater complexity. In most applications, the token ring also requires more cable than a bus because of the need to close the loop to all stations.

As with the token bus, a token is continually circulating throughout the network. When a station receives the token, which is a three-octet block, it is entitled to send if it has data equal to or higher in priority than the token indicates. At the end of its message, the transmitting station generates a new token that can be seized by the next station in the ring if it possesses the necessary priority. Data is transmitted bit by bit around the ring. The addressee station(s) copies the frame and transmits it. When the transmitting station receives its own message, it removes it from the ring and checks for the addressee's acknowledgement.

ACTIVE MONITOR

One station on the ring is always designated as the active monitor to oversee the health of the network. The active monitor, besides serving its terminals, is assigned the overall supervisory function for the network. It is responsible for error recovery, for detecting the absence of valid frames of data, for detecting the absence of a token, and for detecting a persistently circulating priority token or a persistently circulating frame.

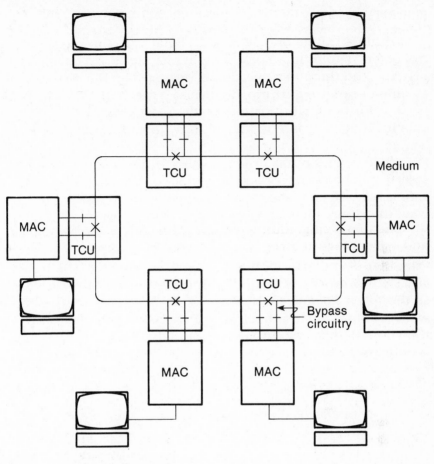

MAC   Media access control
TCU   Trunk coupling unit

FIGURE 11.3   IEEE 802.5 token ring

Although only one station is designated as the active monitor, all stations contain active monitor logic, but keep it on standby in case it is needed. If the active monitor fails, the station first detecting the failure initiates action to assume the role. It begins by entering a claim token mode and sends a claim token message on the network. If the claim token returns to the originating station, with a message containing its own address, it knows it has been the first to detect the failure. It then generates a new token and assumes the active monitor role.

PRIORITY SETTING

Within a frame, one octet is designated as the access control octet. Within that block of eight bits, three are devoted to priority, and three to reservation. Messages on the system are assigned one of eight priority levels. When a station's traffic has a priority equal to or higher than the priority of the circulating token, it is entitled to seize the token and send a frame.

When a station has priority traffic to send, it changes the reservation bits as it repeats the access control field. The reservation bits are changed to the highest priority traffic. In this way, the reservation bit is set at the highest priority level on the queue for entry to the network. When a token circulates through a station with traffic of a priority equal to or greater than that of the priority bits, that station can seize the token and send priority traffic until a timer within its MAC, known as the *token holding timer,* expires. In this manner, the network is able to ensure that traffic during heavy load periods is transmitted up to system capacity, and that low priority traffic is deferred.

FRAME STRUCTURE

The structure of the frame is similar to the token bus (see Figure 11.4). The starting delimiter is a one-octet block of set pattern. As we discussed above, the access control block is a single octet that contains priority and reservation information. Frame control, which defines the type of frame, is a one-octet block, followed by destination and source addresses. These blocks, identical in format to the CSMA/CD and token bus addresses, can be designated as individual, group, or broadcast addresses.

The information block has no maximum length in a token ring. Each MAC in the ring contains a token holding timer, which specifies the maximum time the station can hold the token before relinquishing it to the next station. When a station has seized the token, it is entitled to send data for the duration of its authorized holding time, provided the data is equal to or of higher priority than that of the token. The information block is followed by a 32-bit CRC block, a one-octet

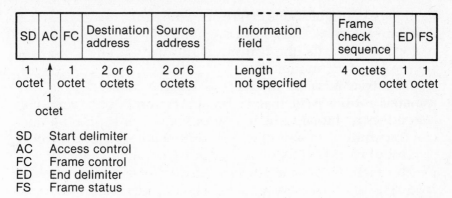

SD	AC	FC	Destination address	Source address	Information field	Frame check sequence	ED	FS
1 octet	1 octet	1 octet	2 or 6 octets	2 or 6 octets	Length not specified	4 octets	1 octet	1 octet

SD   Start delimiter
AC   Access control
FC   Frame control
ED   End delimiter
FS   Frame status

FIGURE 11.4   IEEE 802.5 token ring frame format

end-of-frame sequence block, an ending delimiter, and a one-octet frame status block.

Because each station on the network repeats the data, the range of the network is greater than that possible with a bus network. However, the fact that each station is a repeater makes the network potentially vulnerable to the failure of a single station. To prevent network failure when a station fails, each station is capable of entering a bypass state through circuitry in the trunk coupling unit. The distance between stations, therefore, cannot exceed the signaling range between alternate stations.

DATAPOINT ARCNET

The IEEE standards are so new that there have been few, if any, commercial applications of standard token-passing networks to date. However. Datapoint's ARCNET is the oldest commercial LAN with over 5,000 installations. It uses a token-passing protocol on a coaxial bus and modified star network with stations connected in a logical ring. The ARCNET protocol was originally proprietary, but Datapoint has opened it for use by other manufacturers. Its token protocol is substantially different from the 802.4 standard.

ARCNET operates at a data rate of 2.5 mb/s. The maximum diameter, limited by propagation speed, is four miles. Some hardware configurations can restrict the range to less than the maximum. Figure 11.5 shows the network consisting of three major components: the transmission medium, hubs, and resource interface modules.

The transmission medium is coaxial cable that is terminated in hubs, which are coaxial junction boxes. Datapoint also offers an infrared light system known as Light Link that can transmit up to one mile over a noncoherent light beam.

Hubs are of two types. Active hubs, containing amplifiers, can be mounted as far apart as 2,000 feet and can support from 8 to 16 ports. Passive hubs, which have no amplifier, are limited to a signaling range of 200 feet and support four ports. Hubs are designed to cause no signal reflections and to introduce no signal loss to the network.

The ports are connected to resource interface modules (RIMs), which correspond to the media access controller in

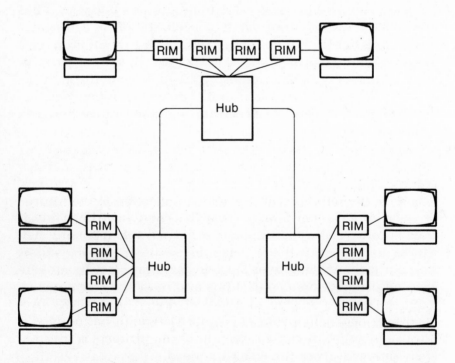

RIM   Resource interface module

FIGURE 11.5   Datapoint ARCNET baseband token passing LAN

802 networks. The RIM is a microprocessor-based device that controls transmission, monitors errors, and handles system reconfiguration. A 1,000-byte buffer is contained in each RIM for storing received messages for connection to application processors. ARCNET can support up to 255 RIMs, and each application processor can support up to 24 terminals. The hubs are interconnected by a bus, and the RIMS are connected to the hubs in a star configuration.

Tokens are passed from station to station in ARCNET in a manner similar to the 802.4 standard. When a station receives the token it transmits an inquiry to the receiving RIM to determine if it has buffer storage space available. If it does not, the receiver returns a NACK (no acknowledge) message. When the sender receives the NACK, it passes the token and waits for the next round to send. If an ACK (acknowledge) message is received, meaning the receiver has buffer space available, a packet of up to 260 bytes is sent. If the packet is received error free, the receiving station responds with an ACK message. If the receiver detects an error, however, it ignores the message and the sending station retransmits the next time it receives the token.

SUMMARY

Advocates of both CSMA/CD and token passing are vigorous in support of their methods. Although some advocates of each method claim that two standards are unnecessary, both methods will find wide application in the future. Token passing will predominate where delays cannot be tolerated, as in many industrial processes. CSMA/CD will be attractive in many light office operations where terminals share files, printers, and other peripherals and in which occasional delays can be tolerated in exchange for lower cost and ease of application.

The choice between the methods can be made only after a thorough analysis of your own application. However, the access method and topology are only two of the considerations. You must also decide the type of signaling to use, a subject we explore next.

12

Baseband Local Area Networks

In a baseband network, data is pulsed directly on the transmission medium at a high rate of speed. The principle is the same as the direct application of high speed data to cable (discussed in Chapter 5) under pulse code modulation concepts. The modulation method is independent of both the transmission medium and the access method; the IEEE standards allow both token passing and CSMA/CD to be used on any transmission medium and with either baseband or broadband modulation. In this chapter we discuss baseband modulation and its application in the local networks including a range of new products collectively known as personal computer networks (PCNs).

TECHNOLOGY OF BASEBAND NETWORKS

The baseband modulation technique is simple. Its signal consists of direct current pulses at the data transfer speed of the network. Baseband and broadband networks are able to accept identical pulses from the terminal, but the transceivers are different. In a baseband system the transceiver is a simple cable driver that matches the impedance of the cable and transmits pulses at the data transfer rate. In a broadband network the pulses are used to modulate a radio frequency carrier. Compared to broadband networks, baseband networks are less expensive because they have no tuned circuits to add to the cost and the design is inherently less complex.

The primary disadvantage to baseband LANs is that capacity is less than with broadband. In a broadband network capacity is expanded by placing the equivalent of several baseband networks on multiple subcarriers.

A baseband network comprises three categories of equipment—the terminals, the media-access control apparatus, and the transmission medium. When data comes from the terminal it is formed into packets, which are pulsed directly on the transmission medium. The active components of the network interface units are frequently mounted directly on the cable to gain the benefits of maximum bandwidth and maximum distance. Packets are broadcast through the network, claimed by the addressee, and delivered to the designated terminal.

Any of the three physical transmission media, paired copper wire, coaxial cable, or fiber optic cable can be used in a baseband network. Copper wire is the least expensive and easiest medium to install, but its bandwidth limitations and susceptibility to noise makes it a choice for short-range and low speed applications only.

Coaxial cable is the most common transmission medium for baseband networks. The network manufacturers' recommendations should be followed for the type and grade of cable to purchase. Generally, the higher the data rate the better the quality of coax required. Baseband networks such as Ethernet require special 50 ohm low loss coaxial cable, which is more expensive than that used for CATV service.

Use care in installing a cable for a baseband network; high data rate applications make network performance vulnerable to damage. If a cable is kinked, mashed or twisted, its electrical characteristics can be changed, causing impedance irregularities that reflect the signal. In the worst case, a station can detect its own reflected signal as an apparent collision each time it attempts to transmit.

Cable segments must be terminated in their characteristic impedance because unterminated or short-circuited cables also cause reflections. Cable used in a baseband network must be grounded only once because multiple grounds can cause transmission errors. Therefore, it is important that the outer jacket of the insulating sheath be kept intact and that coaxial connectors be insulated from ground.

Fiber optic cable is also a feasible transmission medium for baseband networks. The data pulses drive a light transmitter, which is analogous to the cable driver in a coaxial network. The light is turned on and off corresponding to the zeros and ones of the data signal. The rapid on/off pulses of light are inherently a baseband modulation method, although it is also possible to modulate fiber optics in a broadband mode as well by using multiple carriers.

In the past, splicing and terminating problems have hampered the use of fiber optics in a local network, but as we shall see in a later section, these problems are being overcome with new developments. Fiber optics will have an increasingly important, possibly a dominant, role in baseband LANs in the future.

PERSONAL COMPUTER NETWORKS

The rapid growth in personal computers (PCs) has generated a substantial demand for networks. The PC environment finds a need to link these devices in order to communicate with one another and share high-cost peripherals such as disk files and letter quality printers. There is also a need for PCs to communicate with mainframe computers for access to corporate data bases, but in this mode the PC is generally playing the role of a dumb terminal. The primary PC network requirement comes from the need of a resource-sharing environment to obtain access to high cost peripherals and, thereby, avoid shuffling floppy disks between users.

One of the primary user objectives in acquiring a PC network is to avoid the problem of an unreliable data base. Even if a file is small enough to be kept on a floppy disk, passing around copies of the disk is risky. The best way for users to be certain they are operating with the latest issue of the file is for all to access a single source. PCNs offer an effective way of meeting this requirement: the different vendor products share a common feature in the file server for the sharing of files. The file server can be a dedicated computer with an attached disk file, a special purpose server, or one of the PCs attached to the network with a file designated for sharing by others.

Most PCNs also provide a print server to allow all users to share a common high quality printer. For draft purposes it is usually most economical to attach a dot-matrix printer to the individual PC, but letter quality printers are too expensive for dedicated use. With a high quality printer on the PCN, users can avoid passing disks to a station equipped with a letter quality printer.

One of the primary objectives of all PCNs is to provide the capability of sharing these peripherals at low cost. Therefore, virtually all such networks are baseband signaling because it is the least costly and most adaptable to a simple network. PCNs operate on coax, twisted pair wire, or flat ribbon cable. Any of the common topologies can be used, and both contention and token passing protocols are implemented. We will describe typical commercial applications of each type of PCN later in this chapter.

In addition to the common hardware interfaces of the print and file servers, many PCNs offer specialized software as well. Electronic mail and messaging are the most common applications. In many small offices, efficiency can be improved through communications over a network, as opposed to the endless exchange of paper. Little communication in a small office occurs in real time. Instead, specialized software handles messages, stores information on a bulletin board, circulates announcements, and performs other such functions that have been typically performed on pieces of paper.

DIFFERENCES BETWEEN PCNS AND LANS

Although PCNs and LANs are designed for the same general purpose and use similar technology, there are distinct differences between the two. The most significant differences are:

1. PCNs operate at a lower data rate than LANs and support lower throughput.
2. No standards exist for PCNs. Each design is proprietary.
3. PCNs use a less expensive transmission medium than most

LANs and, therefore, are less expensive and easier to install.

4. In many PCNs the media access controller plugs directly into the bus or expansion slot in the PC. This means the PCN will be compatible only with PCs for which it is designed.

5. Many PCNs are entirely self-contained and have no gateways to public networks or PBXs. To use the PC in an off-net application can require its removal from the PCN and its connection to another network through a modem.

6. Security is often weak on PCNs. Unless the application program has a built-in security provision, it can be difficult to restrict users from accessing files. In some cases confidential files must be kept off the network.

PCNs generally operate at a much lower data speed than full-fledged LANs. Therefore, they are capable of supporting fewer terminals than LANs; with high activity, their throughput falls short of that provided by LANs. Before acquiring one, therefore, your data communications requirements should carefully be evaluated to ensure that the network will not be overloaded at the outset.

Because PCNs are designed for economy and for only a limited number of stations, they do not conform to 802 LAN standards. Although some of the protocols resemble 802 standards, each is proprietary. Thus it will be difficult or impractical to add nonsupported PCs to the network.

Also, modifications to the PC's operating system is required in most networks. Operating systems such as Microsoft's MS-DOS and PC-DOS are not designed for multi-user application, and most networks add a control layer to the operating system to allow users to share common resources without interfering with one another. These modifications can generate incompatibilities with some application software.

PCN COSTS

The price of a PCN can range from approximately $500–$3000 per station. Comparing PCNs on the basis of costs, however, can be difficult because to do so you must deter-

mine what is included in the purchase price and what is required to implement the network. For example, some PCNs require a dedicated file server or a dedicated computer to act as
a file server. If the PC cannot be used as a work station, it
becomes part of the cost of the total network. All networks
have a basic "getting started" price that must be shared among
the stations. If only a few stations are connected, the price per
station will be high, but the incremental cost of adding a station may be only the cost of the controller board. The cost of
PCNs is primarily related to the cost of dedicated servers, the
number of work stations on the network, and the additional
features available such as gateway servers. A full-featured PCN
approaches the cost of a LAN.

Evaluate software costs carefully. If the network is incompatible with existing software, replacing it can be a substantial
cost penalty.

Cost of installation and upkeep deserves serious consideration. Many PCNs are sufficiently simple to install yourself.
However, the seller of a do-it-yourself network may have little
capability to maintain it; you may find yourself investing in
test equipment to detect faults in the medium and buying
spare controller boards to substitute for defective ones
returned to the vendor for repair.

Compatibility with future software releases can add to the
cost of the network. For example, the majority of the PCs currently on the market are designed to operate with MS-DOS, PC-
DOS or CP/M operating systems. In acquiring a network, you
must be certain that the manufacturer is committed to supporting future releases of operating systems. Otherwise, you
can find your network tied to an obsolete system with considerable expense required to upgrade or replace it.

EXAMPLES OF BASEBAND LOCAL AREA NETWORKS

In this section we will examine several baseband local area
networks which use a variety of transmission media, and
diverse technology. From these examples, it should become
more clear how baseband LANs are applied in actual practice.

SIECOR FIBERLAN AND UNGERMANN/BASS FIBER OPTIC NET/ONE™

Siecor FiberLAN is one of the first of a growing number of fiberoptic LAN applications. The system is available as a point-to-point network that will transmit video or voice signals on either a frequency division or PCM basis. Siecor provides optical transceivers, cable, and couplers for the Ungermann-Bass Net/One fiber optic Ethernet.

The point-to-point network is equipped with optical transmitters and receivers that can accommodate either PCM or video inputs. An optical transmitter equipped with a light-emitting diode is coupled to one end of the fiber optic cable, and a receiver with an avalanche photo diode detector is coupled to the cable at the receiving end. Two fibers with two transmitter and receiver pairs make up a full system capable of transporting a broadcast quality video signal (10 Hz to 5 mHz). The system is capable of transporting up to 96 digital voice channels or an equivalent number of data channels at distances up to 15 km. (9 miles).

When FiberLAN is applied in the Ungermann-Bass Ethernet, the fiber optic system supplies the equivalent of a coaxial cable in a conventional baseband system. In the coaxial version Net/One connects its Network Interface Units (NIUs) to the cable through baseband transceivers. In the fiber optic version the transceivers are equipped with electro-optical transceivers to convert the baseband pulses to optical pulses. Otherwise, the two systems are conceptually identical.

Two of the major difficulties with using fiber optics in a LAN have been addressed by Siecor. First, the problem of splicing fiber optic cable has been overcome with special fixtures that allow a properly prepared fiber to be inserted for splicing or terminating. The skill level requirements have largely been solved with Siecor's techniques because the cable is not spliced in the conventional manner. The fiber is scored with a special cleaver and broken squarely for insertion into a special splicing fixture.

Second, the difficulty of tapping fiber in a bus topology has been solved by terminating the fibers in central hubs known as reflective stars or transmissive stars. A reflective star is a passive device that reflects light from the end of a fiber into all the other fibers terminated in the star. When the network is idle, all terminals hold their LED transmitters in a nonemitting state. When a terminal prepares to send a packet, if no light pulse is present it assumes that it is clear to send; in the standard Ethernet manner, it pulses a packet toward the star. The star reflects the pulses into all the other legs terminated in it. The light pulses are broadcast to terminals simultaneously, then are converted to electrical pulses, and finally are detected by the addressee in the same manner as a coaxial cable Ethernet.

The reflective star offers the simplicity and reliability of a passive device, but introduces loss into the network. This limits the number of fibers that can be terminated in this manner, and thus limits the size of the network. This limitation can be minimized with a transmissive star, which is an active element. By using transmissive stars, the full Ethernet specification of 1,024 terminals can be met. As many as 62 NIUs can be connected per star with the capability of forming more complex networks by interconnecting stars. In a single star configuration NIUs can be up to 2,800 meters (1.7 miles) apart.

FiberLAN enables the use of a wider network diameter than coaxial Ethernets because of the higher propagation speed of the fiber. With the reflective star there is a tradeoff between network diameter and the number of nodes on the network because of the loss of the star. Both the splices and the stars can be stored in a cross connect point known as a Fiber Wiring Center (FWC)™. The FWC is placed at appropriate branching locations to provide a connecting point for grouping fibers much as a cross connect terminal is used for connecting twisted pair wire.

Figure 12.1 illustrates a typical application of FiberLAN in an office complex. Multi-strand fiber is buried directly between buildings. FWCs are placed in one or more locations in each building to distribute the fiber among the terminals. At the FWC, the fibers radiating to terminal locations can be assigned for point-to-point use of data, voice, or video, or to LAN use.

The advantage of an architecture such as this is its expandability. If cable of the proper grade and size is placed initially, there is little reason the cable should not provide an organi-

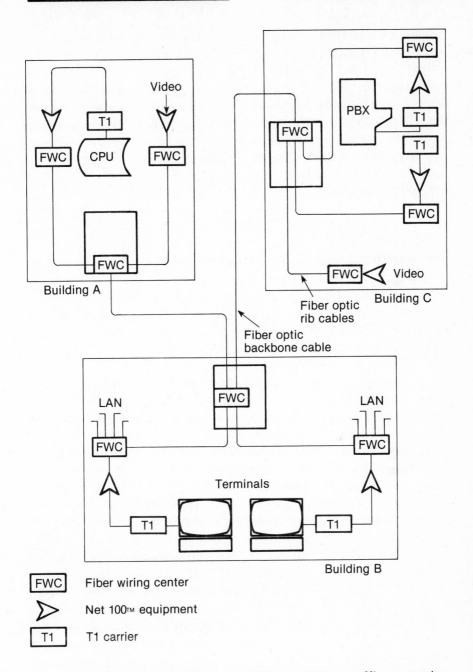

FIGURE 12.1   Application of FiberLAN in an office complex

zation with its ultimate communication capability without further cable additions.

When fiber is placed in this configuration, the network topology can easily be changed. Assume an organization starts with a baseband bus network wired in a star configuration as shown in Figure 12.2. If the network is outgrown in a few years, the bus can be easily split at the FWCs and wired into separate networks. If a token ring topology is needed later, the bus can be converted by resplicing the star into a ring as shown in Figure 12.2.

3COM ETHERSERIES™

A growing number of products aimed at networking personal computers is entering the market. One PCN that has received favorable acclaim is the 3Com EtherSeries, a network that is designed to be compatible with Ethernet-compatible devices. In its initial configurations, the 3Com is designed for application with the IBM Personal Computer. With the popularity of the PC, it is likely to find wide use.

The media access controller (3Com calls it EtherLink) is contained in a card that plugs into the PC. Etherlink™ comes in two versions, *thick Ethernet* and *thin Ethernet*. The thin version uses RG 58/U cable, which is .2 inch in diameter, flexible, and inexpensive. This version is limited to 100 terminals and a maximum length of 304 meters, and therefore does not meet the full IEEE 802.3 standard.

The thick cable version uses standard Ethernet cable, which is .4 inch in diameter, stiff and more difficult to install, as well as four to five times more costly. Use of the thick cable allows a network diameter of 1000 meters and supports up to 1000 terminals.

In the thin cable 3Com net, the cable is terminated directly in the Etherlink circuit board using a T adapter and BNC twist-lock connectors. With the thick cable network, a transceiver is mounted on the cable and connected to the PC with a separate cable up to 50 feet long.

EtherSeries is initially intended for electronic filing, electronic mail, and for printer-sharing. Processor equipped network servers are required to provide these functions. Filing requires that one station be designated as a file server—an

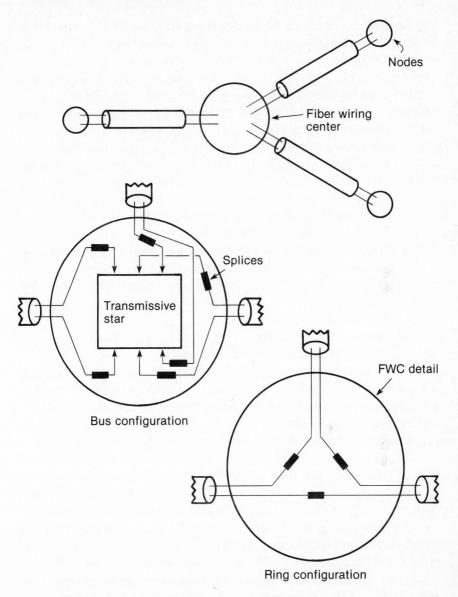

Nodes

Fiber wiring center

Splices

Transmissive star

Bus configuration

FWC detail

Ring configuration

FIGURE 12.2   R configuration of fiber optic from a bus to ring network

IBM XT with an internal hard disk or an IBM PC with an external hard disk. For more capacity, 3Com's AP Network Server with a 30 MB hard disk can be used, or a Digital Equipment Corporation VAX™ computer can act as a file server.

Each user is given an exclusive partition in the file using 3Com's EtherShare™ software. Files can be private for limited users with password access; files can be public for use by all terminals on the network; and files can be shared, that is, accessed simultaneously and read or written by multiple users. Shared files are intended for data base applications that are open to multi-users allowed to read and update the files.

The network file server is addressed as a disk drive. For example, in a PC equipped with two disks, the network would be addressed as disk C. This makes it possible for anyone who knows how to use the computer to access the network. Sending data to the printer is accomplished with an EtherPrint command. If the printer is busy, the server queues messages, groups them by user if so instructed, and puts them out to the printer in turn. With draft and letter quality printers attached to the network, many users can share a limited number of peripherals and save considerable time in transporting disks for a central operator to print.

3Com offers an electronic mail software package to use with the IBM PC. Messages, memos, and files can be sent to other PCs on the network, or they can be sent to the network server, which acts as the central mail box. Messages can be sent to individuals or to all addressees on a list. A built-in editor, part of the EtherMail™ software, can be used to generate a reply to the messages.

CORVUS OMNINET™

Omninet is one of the most widely used PCNs on the market. The network operates at 1 mb/s and uses twisted-pair wire for its transmission medium. Each station is connected to a passive tap with a twisted-pair cable that may be up to 5 meters long. If environmental noise is a problem, shielded cable can be used to give the network approximately the same isolation from interference as coax. The basic cable segments are 330 meters (1000 feet) long. With repeaters the network can span 4,000 feet.

Omninet can accommodate from 2 to 64 PCs and is compatible with most of the major computers on the market. PCs are connected over an RS 232-C or RS-449 interface to a *transporter* wired to the cable tap. The transporter implements the first to the fourth layers of the OSI model, taking its name from the fourth layer, the transport layer. Station addresses are set with a dip switch on the transporter interface card. The transporter performs the functions of transmitting and, if necessary, retransmitting messages, checking errors, and acknowledging receipt of messages, as well as detecting duplicate messages.

The network operates with a protocol known as CSMA/CA (collision avoidance). A station, operating through its transporter, senses the status of the network transmission path. If the path is clear, it transmits a block to a buffer in the receiving transporter, called a *socket*. Each transporter provides four sockets. If the block is received correctly, the transporter sends an acknowledgment. If an acknowledgment is not received within a time-out interval, the station resends the message, and continues to resend until it receives an acknowledgment or exceeds a threshold. Since the sending station retains network control until the packet is correctly received, collisions are avoided.

Corvus provides both disk and printer servers for its Omninet. The disk server accommodates up to four disks and can provide on-line storage for 80 megabytes of information.

ORCHID TECHNOLOGY PCNET

PCnet™ is designed for IBM and IBM-compatible computers. It is at the lower end of the cost scale for PCNs. It uses CSMA/CD over 75 ohm coaxial cable and can operate up to 3,000 feet over RG59/U cable, and up to 7,000 feet with RG11/U coax. The network operates at 1 mb/s.

Unlike many other PCNs, PCnet does not require a dedicated file server. Devices on the network are designated as a user PC or as a shared PC. The user PC does not share its resources; the shared PC allows other PCs access to resources such as the hard disk in an IBM XT.

A shared PC can designate certain of its resources as private. In this manner, confidential files can be isolated from unauthorized access. The only security measure the system provides is the ability to restrict a file from the network by keeping it on a private drive.

NESTAR CLUSTER ONE™

Cluster One is offered in two versions: PLAN (personal local area network) 1,000 and PLAN 4000. Plan 1000 is designed for Apple II and Apple III computers running under Apple/DOS, Apple Pascal, or CP/M operating systems. Nestar states that it can handle from 2 to 65 PCs on the network. A file server offers access to a 66 megabyte hard disk and up to 4,000 megabytes of storage with multiple servers. A hard disk cartridge tape backup and print server to handle up to four printers are optionally available.

PLAN 1000 uses CSMA/CD over a 16-conductor flat ribbon cable to interface the PCs in a bus or star configuration. Eight conductors of the cable are used for data and six for control. Data is transmitted between stations at a data rate of 240 kb/s. Because the bits are transmitted in parallel, the data rate is considerably higher than a serial data transfer method.

PLAN 4000 can accommodate up to 255 PCs at 2.5 mb/s over coaxial cable using a token passing protocol. The network has a range of up to 6.5 km (4 miles). Its controller plugs directly into Apple or IBM PC—compatible computers. The heart of the system is a file server equipped with a 60 mbyte hard disk. Optional disk storage with multiple files can go as high as 548 mbytes with a cartridge tape backup for the disk.

Besides print and file servers, PLAN 4000 offers a variety of other servers including gateways to other networks, a 3270 (IBM) emulation server, a TELEX server, and a 3780 (IBM) server that emulates bisynchronous protocols. PLAN 4000 offers more features and options than most other PCNs and therefore is at the high end of the price range for such networks.

INTERLAN NET/PLUS™

The Interlan NET/PLUS is a local area network meeting the Ethernet IEEE 802.3 specification. It is available in two configurations with software that is compatible with several popular minicomputers and personal computers. Any RS 232-C device and personal computers with the required software can be coupled to the network through the Interlan NTS10 Terminal Server. Supported minicomputers are connected through Ethernet controllers that plug into their bus systems. Terminal servers and Ethernet controllers are connected to the coaxial cable through transceiver units that are mounted directly on the coax and coupled to the terminal device over cable as long as 50 feet.

Figure 12.3 illustrates a typical configuration of the network using NTS10 Terminal Servers. The NTS10 provides up to eight asynchronous ports for connection to RS 232-C devices, including personal computers, printers, plotters, terminals and modems. The devices contend for access to the network through the terminal server.

The ports are symbolically named for ease of use. Each port has a physical address that is used by the system, but the

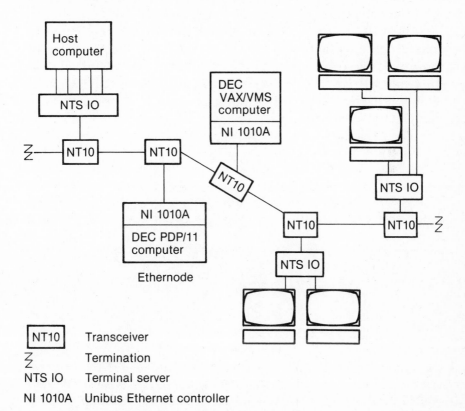

FIGURE 12.3   Interlan NET/PLUS contention network

network translates the internal address to a symbolic address that is assigned by the network manager. Users address the network with a command language. For example, a user establishes a switched virtual circuit to a network device with the command CALL to the appropriate address. Connections are broken with the command DISCONNECT. An on-line menu can be accessed with the command HELP.

The NTS10 enables devices with different baud rates or connector configurations to be interconnected. After it has been configured to the attached device, the NTS10 can perform the required translations to allow the device to communicate with another at a different speed over the 10 mb/s Ethernet. Connections can be established between terminals on either a switched virtual circuit basis where the connection is established with each session, or on a permanent virtual circuit basis where two devices are attached to each other until the network manager terminates the connection.

The NT10 transceiver unit can be mounted directly on the coaxial cable while the system is in operation. The first step in mounting the transceiver is to drill holes in opposite sides of the cable with a drill guided by a special fixture. The fixture is attached to the cable with a block as shown in Figure 12.4. As

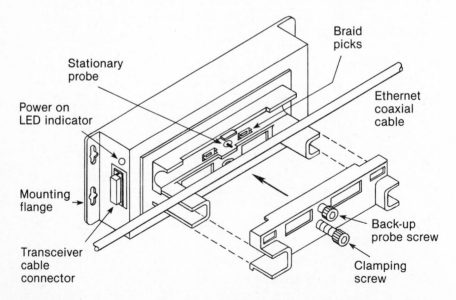

FIGURE 12.4   Mounting the Interlan NET/PLUS NT10 transceiver

the Allen screw holding the two halves of the clamp is tightened, a probe mounted on the stationary portion of the block pierces the center conductor of the cable as the braid picks make contact with the other sheath. Then the backup probe screw is tightened to form a second contact with the center conductor. The transceiver is cabled to the terminal server (or to the controller if the compatible minicomputer version is used) and the connection is complete.

The Interlan network is available for Digital Equipment Corporation VAX and PDP-11 computers, Data General Nova, Eclipse, and MV Series computers, and for computers using the Intel Multibus system. Several versions of Digital, Apple, Xerox, IBM and Radio Shack personal computers are also supported. Consult the manufacturer about compatibility with different systems.

13

Broadband Local Networks

In discussions of local networks, debate often centers on whether broadband or baseband is the superior technology. More has been made of the differences between the two modulation methods than the facts warrant. In practice, both can use the same multiple access techniques, similar transmission media and equivalent topologies. The primary difference between the two is that baseband networks pulse data signals directly on the transmission medium while broadband networks pulse data signals on a radio frequency (RF) carrier. By using multiple RF carriers broadband networks can make use of the entire frequency spectrum capability of the transmission medium. This additional capacity comes at a price—broadband networks are more costly. Other than that, the differences between the two techniques are important only insofar as the cable can be required for other than LAN functions. In fact, some networks, as we shall see, can be converted from baseband to broadband without a great deal of effort.

TECHNOLOGY OF BROADBAND NETWORKS

Broadband networks use cable television (CATV) hardware to carry one or more multiple access channels in addition to other services. A properly designed coaxial cable and

163

amplifier system is capable of passing frequencies from about 5 MHz to 400 MHz as shown in Figure 13.1. Television channels each occupy 6 MHz of bandwidth. Therefore, a single coax offers the capacity to handle more than 60 one-way television channels. Many organizations install coax for closed-circuit television, training, security, and other such applications. A properly designed cable can accommodate a local area network and transmit point-to-point multiplexed voice, data, and television channels as well.

A CATV system is inherently a one-way transmission medium. The amplifiers, which are designed to pass broad analog signals, can amplify in only one direction. Bidirectional amplifers are available, but the transmitting and receiving signals must be separated. In contrast, baseband systems broadcast in both directions simultaneously. To make bidirectional transmission possible with a broadband system, provision must be made for carrying the reverse direction.

Consider the simple broadband system illustrated in Figure 13.2. Television channel 2 is used for closed-circuit television. The signal travels from the scanning camera to monitors 1 and 2. Bridged to the cable, the monitors can receive a signal by tuning to channel 2. On channel 3, data terminal A can transmit to B or C without difficulty because they are located in the forward direction of the amplifier. However, B and C cannot respond to A's messages in the reverse direction because the amplifier blocks them.

The reverse direction can be handled by one of two methods. Either the system must send on one cable and receive on a separate cable, or the sending frequencies must

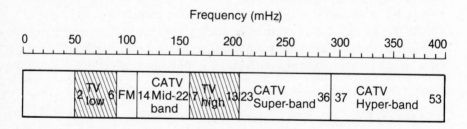

FIGURE 13.1 Cable television frequency allocation

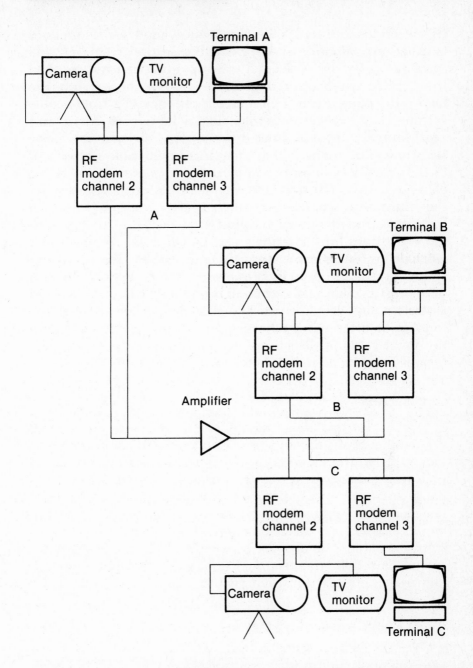

FIGURE 13.2   Typical broadband network

be shifted to a different receiving frequency. The first method is called a dual cable system, and the second a single cable system. Equipment is needed to couple the transmit cable to the receive cable in a dual cable system, or to shift the transmit frequency to the receive frequency in a single cable system. In CATV terminology, this is known as **head end equipment,** a term that has been adopted by local networks. Head end equipment, which exists in a single cable system and in the amplifiers of all broadband systems, consists of active elements. Although they are reliable, a failure can interrupt the entire network.

A broadband system resembles baseband in that one or more of the 6 MHz channels can be set aside for local networks. A contention channel using CSMA/CD access, and resembling Ethernet in most respects, can be assigned to one of the 6 MHz channels. Although broadband can be laid out in a straight bus architecture like baseband, a branching tree topology is often used. Wherever side legs are extended from the main cable, a directional coupler is used to ensure the proper impedance match between cable sections.

CABLE TAPS

Since resistive taps radiate more RF energy than FCC regulations allow, the taps used to connect the network interface units to the cable conform to higher quality standards than the ordinary resistive taps used for baseband. Also, in damp environments typical of CATV, taps can admit water to penetrate the cable and cause damage. Consequently, broadband networks use directional couplers to isolate the stations from the cable. The taps are passive, with the active circuitry placed closed to the terminal equipment so that a station failure will not disrupt the network.

RF MODEMS

Terminals in a broadband network are interfaced to the transmission medium through radio frequency (RF) modems. A modem applies the data signal to the medium at a radio carrier frequency. The principle is the same as with analog multiplexing described in Chapter 5. Each RF modem contains a transmitter tuned to the network transmit frequency and a receiver tuned to the network receive frequency.

Broadband networks contain two types of RF modems. A fixed frequency modem is capable of operating on only one frequency. A frequency agile modem is capable of shifting between channels. The frequency allocations are made by a controller that is able to monitor the busy/idle status of the RF channels. When a terminal signals its desire for connection to another terminal, the controller selects an idle channel, directs the two modems to the proper frequency, and drops out of the connection. Used in this manner, a broadband network is similar to circuit switching.

In evaluating broadband networks, it is important to note the efficiency of the RF modem in bandwidth utilization. For example, although a modem can handle a data rate of 1.544 mb/s, and while it is possible to put this bandwidth in 772 kHz by using two bits per Hz encoding, the modem may not be capable of this kind of data encoding. While a 6 MHz TV channel theoretically could support seven 1.544 mb/s channels, some manufacturers may be capable of putting only one 1.544 mb/s channel on a TV channel because of hardware limitations. The ultimate capacity of a broadband network depends on the amount of bandwidth available in the transmission medium and the efficiency of the RF modems in utilizing the bandwidth.

BANDPASS SPLITTING

Unless the broadband network is devoted solely to data and voice transmission, it will have a certain amount of one-way TV traffic. If a dual cable system is used, the entire bandwidth of the system, as shown in Figure 13.1, is available in either direction. With single cable systems, the bandwidth can be split in one of three ways. Figure 13.3a shows the sub-split system, which allocates most of the bandwidth to TV transmission and only a small amount for data. The high-split system of 13.3c divides the bandwidth equally. The compromise mid-split shown in Figure 13.3b is endorsed by the IEEE.

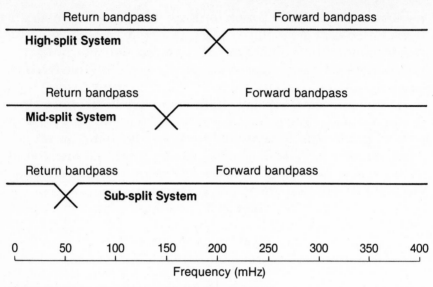

FIGURE 13.3   Broadband frequency splits

ONE CABLE OR TWO?

The selection of a single or dual cable system is a matter of two variables—your requirements, and the system used by the manufacturer. The single cable system is physically less complex and is used by most vendors. Figure 13.4 shows the network of splitters, amplifiers and taps for a single cable system, while Figure 13.5 shows a similar network for a dual cable system. Because dual cables are installed in parallel, they must be accurately identified as send and receive cables, or tracing faults will be difficult.

BROADBAND LANs

Within a broadband system, certain channels can be set aside for video and voice transmission, with one or more channels reserved for a CSMA/CD or token-passing channel. Messages or packets are sent and received from a LAN channel exactly as they are with a baseband network except that the channel is applied to an RF carrier, and the transmit and receive channels are separated.

The same distance limitations apply, and the same problems of collision detection and recovery occur with a broadband network as with a baseband network with a few additional complications. In a baseband network collisions are detected on a direct current basis. Broadband networks, which are incapable of passing direct current, must use a different method of collision detection. A common technique is for the station to listen on the receive cable or frequency to

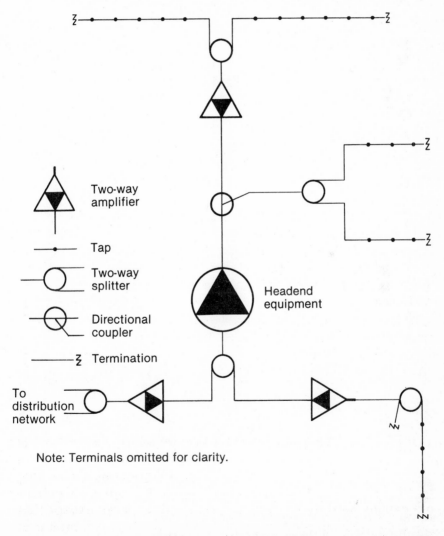

Two-way amplifier

Tap

Two-way splitter

Directional coupler

Termination

Headend equipment

To distribution network

Note: Terminals omitted for clarity.

FIGURE 13.4   Single cable broadband network

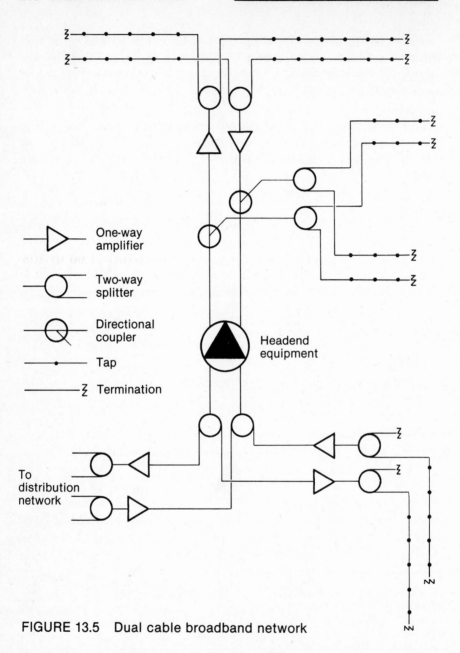

FIGURE 13.5   Dual cable broadband network

see if its transmission was damaged by collision. This reduces network throughput somewhat compared with baseband. Throughput is also reduced by the added length of the doubled cable. These two factors plus higher cost are the most important drawbacks of a broadband network.

Offsetting these disadvantages are technical advantages. Two of the most important are that broadband minimizes the phase and amplitude distortion present in baseband transmission and avoids most low frequency noise.

POINT-TO-POINT BROADBAND NETWORKS

If an organization has enough volume to warrant it, point-to-point traffic can be applied to a broadband network. The division can be accomplished with analog frequency division multiplexing, or with digital time division multiplexing. Both systems use a device known as a **channel bank** to divide the spectrum. A frequency division channel bank assigns 12 channels at 4 kHz intervals to a frequency spectrum of 60 to 108 kHz. Figure 13.6 shows how this *group* frequency can be further multiplexed. A channel bank is a two-way communication device. To obtain the needed full-duplex communication, which is required for all voice and most data applications, equivalent frequencies must be assigned in both directions.

Time division channel banks, also known as digital channel banks, sample voice and create 24 channels at 64 kb/s on a 1.544 mb/s stream (discussed in Chapter 5). Using a multiplexer, it is possible to digitize 24 channels of voice and, by using a 2-bits-per-Hertz modulation system, to modulate it into 772 kHz of frequency spectrum.

Channel banks, which are designed for high-grade telephone service, are an expensive way of dividing the CATV spectrum. Within the narrow range covered by most local networks, channel banks will usually be found to be an expensive alternative to voice frequency circuits on twisted-pair cable. When right of way is difficult to obtain, when construction for crossing streets and other obstructions is costly, and as the distance between terminals increases, channelizing CATV becomes increasingly attractive.

APPLICATIONS FOR BROADBAND NETWORKS

Although baseband and broadband local networks overlap to some degree in their applications, for most organizations the choice between the two will be clear. It should be evi-

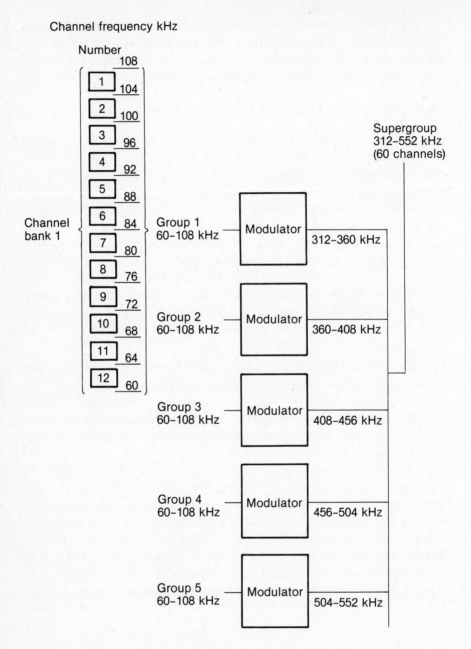

FIGURE 13.6   Analog modulation system

dent that there is little difference to the user between a LAN implemented on a baseband network and one implemented on a broadband network. The primary difference is that the wider bandwidth of a broadband cable offers the opportunity to create multiple LANs if they are needed. One reason for selecting broadband is that the application is too large for single baseband cable.

Organizations needing video communications or having closed-circuit TV already installed will likely find broadband the preferable medium because data communications can be added for little extra cost. Organizations transporting a considerable amount of point-to-point data will find that broadband offers the ability to establish numerous circuits over a cable.

By implementing frequency agile modems, a broadband network can provide the equivalent of circuit switching for communication requirements that are too heavy for CSMA/CD but too light to warrant a dedicated channel. However, the frequency agile modems require a central controller and are more expensive than the fixed frequency transceivers used in CSMA/CD or in point-to-point service.

Broadband channels are also useful when the range exceeds the allowable diameter of a baseband channel. Although the same distance considerations that limit the use of CSMA/CD apply equally to baseband and broadband networks, point-to-point channels can be extended on CATV throughout a metropolitan area.

Offsetting these advantages is the higher cost of broadband networks. All elements of the network except the cable are more expensive: A broadband network can cost more than twice as much per channel as baseband.

VIDEO TRANSMISSION ON BROADBAND NETWORKS

The claim that broadband systems are superior in handling video is based on the assumption that analog video is being transmitted. Presently analog is the most cost-effective method for video transmission, although the technology of digitized video is advancing rapidly.

The techniques used in broadcast television generate analog signals. The cost of the 6 MHz of bandwidth is moderate per channel on a local coaxial distribution system, but to transmit it longer distances, microwave radio or satellite circuits are required. Although video compression equipment is available for digital systems, analog video consumes the entire 6MHz of bandwidth. For closed circuit TV, meetings, security and other such applications, a 6MHz channel is not needed. To save money, most organizations are willing to settle for less than the purity of a full-bandwidth broadcast quality signal.

Equipment currently on the market or under development can compress a digitized video signal into narrow bandwidths. It accomplishes this by processing the signal at each end. Instead of transmitting an entire frame as analog systems do, only the changes from frame to frame are transported. Excellent quality can be obtained over a 1.5 mb/s T1 line. With some sacrifice in clarity, an acceptable signal can be transmitted over half or even one-fourth of a T1 line. Half of a T1 line, you will remember is the equivalent of 12 voice channels.

The tradeoff in video compression is in the ability of the system to handle motion. If some of the participants at a meeting rave and pound the table, they will appear blurred in a picture. But with the camera fixed at a suitable distance, the blurring that occurs during an ordinary conference is hardly noticeable, and charts and graphs can be transmitted with excellent clarity.

Of course the video compression equipment costs more than transmitting a full analog signal. For the next few years, analog TV will remain the most cost-effective way of distributing video signals in a local network. But as line costs increase, and as video processing equipment costs drop, it will become increasingly more cost-effective to send signals digitally.

REPRESENTATIVE BROADBAND NETWORKS

In this section we will look at three networks that demonstrate the range of techniques used to implement broadband networks. Although all three networks use coaxial cable as the transmission medium, fiber optic cable is available as an option for some. One network even offers twisted-pair wire as a baseband for the initial installation with the capability to convert to broadband for future requirements.

CONTELNET™

Earlier in this chapter we observed that the differences between broadband and baseband networks have been somewhat overstated. ContelNet illustrates the similarities between the two systems since it is a network that is convertible from baseband to broadband. An organization can start with a single baseband LAN. As its needs expand to require a separate LAN or closed-circuit television, the system can be converted to broadband.

In its baseband configuration the network uses a conventional Ethernet-like bus topology. CSMA/CD is used for access in either configuration. To convert the network to broadband, cable drivers inside the Bus Interface Unit (BIU) are replaced with radio frequency modems. The cable taps are changed to accommodate the wider bandwidth and to contain RF radiation. CATV head and equipment is added to convert the transmit frequency to the receive frequency so that it can operate in a single cable configuration.

In the baseband configuration, the network can span up to five miles in radius at a 2 mb/s data rate. If it is more than 1,000 feet in diameter, however, amplifiers must be added at 1000-foot intervals when the network is converted to broadband. When the intial baseband system is installed with plans to convert it to a broadband network, the conversion can be simplified by placing connectors on the cable where future amplifiers will be required.

The data rate supported on the baseband version is 2 mb/s. Optionally, the data rate can be increased on the broadband version up to 10 mb/s. Both the broadband and baseband configurations use 75 ohm cable, meaning that the baseband version is not fully compatible with the IEEE standard.

ContelNet also provides the capability of matching either coaxial cable, fiber optics, or twisted-pair wire in the baseband mode. This allows the user to implement the system initially over twisted-pair to save money and later upgrade to the more expensive coaxial cable for expansion.

The network accommodates up to 255 BIUs. Each BIU is equipped with four ports, allowing more than 1,000 terminals to share the network. The BIU contains a microprocessor that can be equipped with a variety of special features. The BIU can interface a network control center (described later) to the network. It can support a file server or a print server to interface shared disk files or printers to the network. The BIU can be equipped with a protocol converter or a gateway unit to interface external networks such as an X.25 packet-switched network, and it performs conversion between ASCII and EBCDIC code sets.

Addressing can be numeric by port number or symbolic. An address can be established as single or rotary. With rotary addressing, if one port is busy the system steps to the next vacant port in the rotary address without the necessity of the user's readdressing the port.

ContelNet can optionally be equipped with a network control center (NCC). This module does not control the flow of traffic but is capable of controlling common functions for administering network performance. For example, the NCC can perform network initialization. It can monitor the status of the nodes, collect network statistics, perform diagnostics, provide alarms to assist in locating system problems.

SYTEK LOCALNET 20™

LocalNet 20 is capable of multiplexing from one to eight contention channels on a single broadband cable. Figure 13.7 shows a typical LAN with Sytek components. LocalNet 20 uses CSMA/CD to access channels at a 128 kb/s data rate over a radius of up to 12 miles. Another Sytek system, LocalNet 40 is based on 2.5 mb/s channels over a narrower radius. A description of each of the components will aid in understanding how the system functions.

The media access controller can be either a 20/100 or a 20/200 Packet Communications Unit (PCU). The PCUs contain frequency agile modems and microprocessor-based controllers. The PCUs are capable of connecting terminals over a virtual circuit to any other port on the same channel. The two models perform the same functions except that the 20/100 is

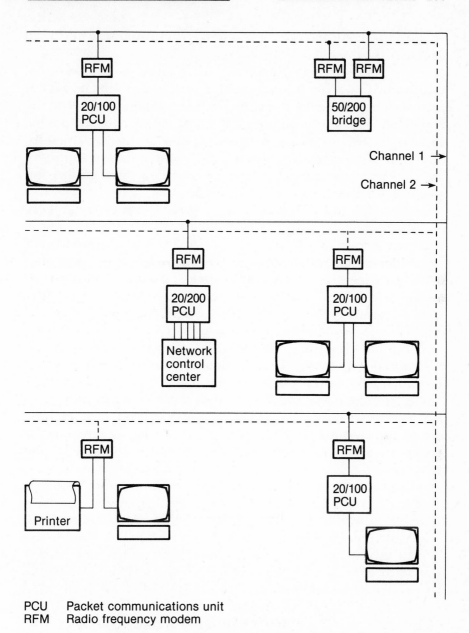

PCU   Packet communications unit
RFM   Radio frequency modem

FIGURE 13.7   Sytek LocalNet 20 broadband network

equipped with two ports, and the 20/200 is capable of multiplexing eight ports to the network through the same transceiver. The transceiver is assigned to the appropriate RF channel by the controller. This channel assignment remains fixed while the terminal is assigned to the same LocalNet 20 channel.

The microprocessor in the PCU interfaces the terminal equipment to the transceiver. It also contains a packet assembler/disassembler for generating packets and receiving them from other terminals. Buffering is included to enable devices to communicate with each other at different speeds. The network design is based on ISO's open system interconnection model so that LocalNet 20 is a complete end-to-end packet-switching network.

The 50/50 unit is a head end frequency converter to connect the low band transmit frequencies of 70 to 106 MHz to the high band receive frequency of 224 to 262 MHz. Regardless of how many LocalNet 20 channels are supported, only one head end unit is required. Protection against head end equipment failure is available through an optional redundant unit that can be manually or automatically switched in service.

When a user's requirements exceed the capacity of one LocalNet 20 channel, additional channels can be formed on different frequencies. Interconnection between channels is accomplished with a 50/200 bridge, which can interconnect as many as eight LocalNet 20 channels. Packets from one channel are stored while the 50/200 connects to the target channel through a frequency agile modem. The 50/200 assigned to the target channel accepts the packet and forwards it to the destination.

The 50/100 unit is a network control center (NCC). The NCC performs overall network management functions such as managing resources, routing traffic, determining node status, and collecting network statistical information. Through the 50/100, gateways to other networks, such as an X.25 packet network, can be provided. Data encryption is also available for security if needed.

WANGNET™

WangNet, a product of Wang Laboratories Inc., is a unique LAN in two respects. First, unlike the majority of broadband systems, WangNet uses a two-cable approach. Although this doubles the amount of cable required and increases the complexity of the distribution system, it more than doubles the available bandwidth. Unlike single cable LANs, WangNet has no active head end equipment. It is necessary only to couple the transmit and receive cables together through a passive head end. Second, the system is unique in its use of the bandwidth. Figure 13.8 shows how the CATV bands are allocated in WangNet.

With WangNet, the capacity of the coaxial cable is divided into four bands. The first, Wang band, is a contention channel intended for ordinary CSMA/CD access among Wang-compatible terminals. Connection to the band is through a cable interface unit (CIU), that creates a communication system based on ISO's open system model and Wang's version of HDLC protocol. Wang band is capable of two modes of operation: one a permanent virtual circuit, and the other a packet-switching mode that Wang refers to as batch file transfer. The CIU performs packet assembly/disassembly and flow control functions.

The peripheral attachment band is intended for interconnecting Wang work stations and peripherals over six broadband channels. Each channel is capable of providing 32 point-to-point circuits. These two bands are not intended for interconnection to equipment made by other manufacturers.

The third channel is the interconnect channel, which is designed for connecting non-Wang equipment on either a switched or point-to-point basis. The switched system uses frequency agile modems to create the connections between users. A device known as a Wang DataSwitch™ performs the channel control functions. The DataSwitch allocates the frequencies for two users to communicate, establishing the connections by controlling the frequency agile modems. Dedicated line services are available over sixty-four 9600 b/s channels or sixteen 64 kb/s channels. Fixed frequency modems are used to create these point-to-point channels.

The fourth band is called the utility band. Seven standard 6 MHz television channels are available on this band for video transmission or other applications requiring this bandwidth. Because of its proprietary use of a large part of the CATV spectrum, WangNet will be of interest primarily to users of Wang office equipment.

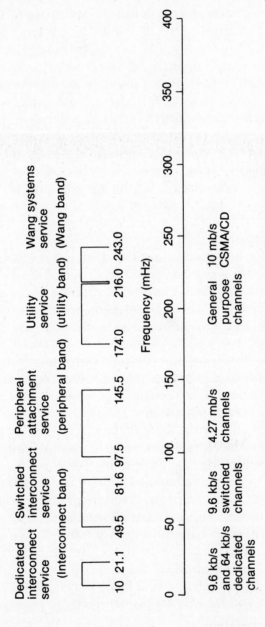

FIGURE 13.8   Frequency utilization in WangNet

14

Maintaining the Local Network

With any type of network, maintenance is a critical factor. The cost penalties for system disruption and outages can be high throughout a network's lifetime. Over the past few years, there are enough options and choices for long-haul network service that users hardly have to consider the effects of network failures. Backup networks are available in most areas. With both metropolitan and long-haul networks redundancy is integral to the design so that service-disrupting failures are rare. Furthermore, since metropolitan and long-haul networks are usually owned by common carriers, the user need not be concerned with maintenance service; it is usually included in the monthly charge. By contrast, local networks are privately owned. It is your organization's responsibility to provide network protection and maintenance, as well as redundancy plans to ensure against system failure.

When industrial and office processes rely on the performance of a local network, your organization's cost performance depends on the network's reliability and in case of failure, on your ability to restore it rapidly. Therefore, maintainability and reliability are two significant factors to consider when selecting a local network. If the cost of a system looks significantly better than its competitors, that is the time to examine it closely. Keep in mind that one way some manufacturers cut costs is by eliminating maintenance features and redundancy.

All this is to say that you must have a maintenance strategy built into the network design. Local networks and the type of organizations they support are so varied that no single maintenance strategy will suffice. This chapter will cover some network maintenance concerns and explain what to look for in evaluating your system requirements.

DESIGN FOR MAINTENANCE

No matter how trouble-free a local network may appear, eventually it will fail or at least parts of it will malfunction, resulting in disrupted service. The network should be laid out to minimize the possibility of failure. Equally important, areas vulnerable to failure should be anticipated. The network should be designed for rapid troubleshooting and restoration.

The first consideration is the physical layout of the transmission medium itself. The cable should be protected from physical damage. The best way to protect it is to conceal it in suspended ceilings, air plenums, and particularly in communications ducts and raceways. If the cabling must be surface mounted in traffic areas, it should be protected by cable guards. Fiber optics and paired copper cable are reasonably insensitive to physical damage, but a coaxial cable can kink if struck by a mail cart, and a kinked cable is enough to disrupt the network.

If the cable includes multiple branches, be sure to keep records of the location of every branching point. At branches the cable should be stored in a cabinet with the terminus of each branch clearly marked. In case of failure, part of the network can be restored by isolating the defective branch (see Figure 14.1.) If a cable is damaged or a streaming terminal begins to litter the network with gibberish (sometimes called the jabber mode), the defective leg can be quickly isolated by disconnecting it at a branching point and replacing it with a termination. Then, with the rest of the network still operating, the defective section can be repaired or replaced.

In dual cable broadband systems, the cables should be

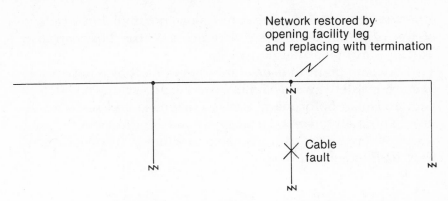

FIGURE 14.1   Fault repair by isolating defective leg

marked with colored rings and embedded tracers to indicate the transmit and the receive cables. If these aren't marked, repair technicians will lose time tracing cables and testing them to find the failed amplifier.

A network with amplifiers or repeaters should be designed for rapid isolation of the defective element. Begin by foreseeing the effects of an element failure and by documenting its probable symptoms. For example, in an Ethernet with two segments connected through a repeater, the inability of the two segments to communicate is a symptom of a failed repeater: Intrasegment communication should be unaffected by repeater failure. In a broadband network, the failure of a repeater or of head end equipment will prevent signals from proceeding beyond the failed unit and effectively disrupt the entire network. You can locate a failed amplifier by patching in spares or by a built-in method of tracing low amplifier output alarms.

The potential of total network failure is inherent in any network with a central controller. It is unlikely that a failure on one leg of a star-connected network can disrupt more than the terminals on that leg. However, the failure of a processor, disk drive, or other central element can cause the entire network to fail. A properly designed network provides redundancy through automatic switching for system components vulnerable to failure.

A multiple processor installation such as the Infotron IS4000 (discussed in Chapter 9) requires a special maintenance strategy. Not only is a processor failure possible, but a failure of the ring that connects the remotes to the host can also disrupt portions of the network.

The main point to bear in mind in evaluating a network is to consider all the ways a failure can occur, assume it will happen, and plan beforehand how to diagnose and restore failures. The maintenance strategy should be documented and stored where it is readily available to either your own or contract maintenance forces.

PREPARE FOR LIMITED SELF-MAINTENANCE

A fast way of getting a failed system back in service is to prepare someone in your organization to do a limited amount of maintenance. When the transmission medium fails, it is especially important to be able to disconnect a failed section and restore as much of the network to service as possible while you are waiting for the vendor to repair the failed component.

Unless the network is extensive and technicians are normally on the premises for other reasons, total self-maintenance is probably too costly to be practical. Extensive training and test equipment are required for complete maintenance, but simple tests can be made using common sense and basic test equipment. Limited self-maintenance requires someone who has received training, has access to good system documentation, and perhaps has simple test equipment.

Some vendors offer training and support for self-maintenance, a factor that you should consider prior to purchasing a system. If the vendor's support is questionable, or if maintenance documentation is not available, you will be at the mercy of the vendor's response time and repair force quality. With smaller and less-established vendors, you are also at the mercy of the vendor's likelihood of remaining in business, which may not be a comforting thought. Any planning for self-maintenance must be done well before failure, and should be considered for any network unless the vendor's repair forces are considered completely dependable.

MAINTENANCE DOCUMENTATION

Caught in a whirl of putting new systems on the market, documentation is frequently given short shrift by many manufacturers. Passive systems such as Ethernet require little documentation, but the more active elements included in broadband networks and circuit-switched networks require a completely documented system. If the vendor should fall prey to the business failures that have characterized the microcomputer industry, a properly documented system may be the only thing that saves a user's system from obsolescence. Let us discuss what documentation you should expect at a minimum.

CABLING DIAGRAMS

A floor plan layout of the network cabling should be created at the time the system is installed and kept up to date with additions and rearrangements. The layout should show the cable route, the location of access points, the location of all taps, branches, splitters, connectors, terminations, amplifiers, head end devices, or any other elements that interrupt the cable. These elements are potential sources of trouble, and a record of their location can save considerable time in pinpointing problems in the transmission medium.

TIME DOMAIN REFLECTOMETER RECORDS

A **time domain reflectometer** (TDR) is used to locate faults in coaxial and fiber optic cables. (In fiber optics the device is called an optical TDR or OTDR.) A TDR is an instrument that sends a short burst of signal down the cable. When it encounters an impedance irregularity, a portion of the signal is reflected back to the source. The TDR displays the fault as a blip on a cathode ray tube that is calibrated in distance to the fault. A TDR works on cable much like radar operates in free space to measure distances to an object that reflects the signal.

In a coaxial or optical fiber cable, as long as the medium is unbroken the return trace will be smooth. Any attached device will show some impedance discontinuity and will reflect on the screen. Faults show vividly and are easy to distinguish from taps and other devices attached to the cable.

You will probably find it worthwhile to make a TDR map of your network when it is installed. If temporary faults are deliberately introduced at known points and a photographic record of the trace of the CRT screen is retained, a technician can use the cabling plan to locate the fault with a minimum of delay.

OTHER SYSTEM DOCUMENTATION

Any other documentation provided by the manufacturer should be retained intact. Most manufacturers do not supply schematic diagrams of replaceable cards, nor are schematics needed because repair of circuit cards is beyond the capabilities of most users. To protect yourself in the event the manufacturer goes out of business or withdraws product support, you should insist on a contract that entitles you to this documentation.

You should also require cabling diagrams of the equipment. For example, the interface between a network interface unit and a terminal may be specified by the manufacturer as standard RS 232-C or RS 449. These interfaces describe standard pin designations, but not all pins are required for most systems. When you attach a new type of terminal to the network, you will need to know what pins are connected at the interface. The manufacturer should provide this information.

A trouble-locating manual is also useful when you must rely on someone other than the vendor's repair forces. This manual should list symptoms and describe how to perform tests and interpret the results. Manufacturers normally prepare such manuals for the use of their technicians, but they usually do not provide them to customers unless it is made a condition of purchase.

Software documentation is equally as important as hardware documentation. For example, most LANs provide methods for reinitializing the system to change addresses and operating characteristics of the media access controllers. PBXs require extensive documentation to initialize the system software with the address numbers, restrictions, and features of each attached station. The local network purchase contract should enumerate each software element and the process for installing changes and updates together with a summary of applicable charges for software service.

MAINTAIN ADEQUATE SPARES

Depending on the design of your local network, you should consider retaining spare components for restoring the system after failures. If the vendor provides assurance under contract that it will retain and provide spares, this step may not be necessary, but it is a factor to consider.

If the transmission medium is of special construction or manufacture, maintain a spare section of cable long enough to span a damaged section as well as connectors and splicing apparatus. Maintain spare amplifiers or replacement cards. Examine any device that is susceptible to failure, and purchase spares to ensure quick and reliable replacement of failed components.

SYSTEM UPGRADES

Most manufacturers continually enhance their systems. This is particularly true of software, which is upgraded to correct defects and to add enhancements. Each manufacturer will have a different policy for handling upgrades. This policy should be evaluated in advance. If you fail to keep the system up to date, you risk being unable to obtain replacements or encountering difficulty in finding repair technicians trained to maintain the system. This is particularly true of systems with central processors and other active elements.

ENVIRONMENTAL CONDITIONS

Totally passive networks can operate in humidity and various temperature conditions without adverse effect. Properly manufactured and installed wire, coax, and fiber optics are immune to temperature variations and the effects of weather. There are exceptions to this rule, but rarely will a local area network test the limits. Broadband amplifiers that have been designed for the temperature extremes of CATV service should survive any LAN environment.

Active elements should be placed only in environments designed to contain electronic equipment. Under temperature extremes, particularly heat, failures can result. Consult the manufacturer's literature when installing a PBX or data switch; be sure the physical environment is within the temperature and humidity extremes specified by the manufacturer. As a rule of thumb, you can expect that electronic equipment will operate in ordinary office temperatures, but processors may require air conditioning. Even though it may appear that the environment will not pose a problem to the network, the manufacturer's specifications for operating temperature and humidity range should be compared to the environmental conditions of your application.

SUMMARY

Give serious consideration to the factors presented in this chapter. We cannot overemphasize their importance. Use the information as evaluation criteria before you lease or buy a local network; it is advisable to write these factors into a specification for selecting the local network. Follow this with a contract that ensures vendor support under mutually agreeable terms. Maintenance considerations are not, however, the only factors that must be included in your list of requirements and specifications. In the next chapter we discuss other factors that you need to evaluate to make your network successful.

15

Developing LAN Requirements and Specifications

Local area network technology is so new and practical experience so limited that selecting the appropriate equipment is an uncertain process. Vendors can help on their systems, but they are not a reliable guide to their own shortcomings. Because each local network application is unique, it is impossible to follow a universal set of requirements; therefore, you must develop your own. The following discussions should provide you with a basis for thinking through your system needs. It will help you to develop a list of requirements and specifications that you can provide vendors competing for your business. In this chapter we will review the factors that will most likely affect your choice of products. Chapter 16 will recommend a process for selecting the system that best meets your requirements.

This chapter is organized into brief discussions around factors that will help you evaluate your needs and understand the impact of the choices open to you.

VOLUME, NATURE, AND GROWTH RATE OF DATA TRAFFIC

Determine your organization's traffic characteristics accurately before you establish your network requirements. If you have a large volume of traffic, it will eliminate some alternative choices. The nature of your business traffic is also important to evaluate. Short, bursty messages are most efficiently handled on a contention network. Bulk data transfer can usually be handled most economically on a point-to-point basis. For terminals with long messages to transmit, a deterministic network such as token passing or circuit switching may be the best solution.

In comparing network designs, it is well to consider the ultimate size of the network; plan with future growth in mind. Sometimes an interim design is the most feasible. For example, a company with a limited number of terminals can often begin a local network most economically by implementing its existing PBX. A new system must either have enough capacity to handle your requirements for several years, or it must be economical to expand.

The process for adding new terminals is an important consideration in evaluating a local network. Token LANs are more complex than contention LANs because the network must be reinitialized with new token routing instructions each time terminals are added. With circuit-switched networks, terminals are usually added easily. However, when processor or switching-network capacity must be added, growth is expensive. In terms of cost, contention networks are somewhere in between. If the cable can be pierced and tapped while in service, growth is not complex. The media access controller must be initialized to recognize the address of its newly added terminal. Otherwise, the addition is accomplished merely by the physical attachment of the station. Most ring networks must be taken out of service to add nodes unless node attachment points with bypasses have previously been installed.

The following criteria can guide you in evaluating network traffic:

- Is message transmission bursty or of long duration?
- Has a traffic study been made? Can you rely on the results?

- Does traffic volume vary during seasons and days of the week?
- How rapidly do you expect the network to grow?
- Will the potential system meet your business needs throughout its design life?
- Will expansion cost be feasible? Will future expansion require a major addition, or does the network grow "gracefully" with each additional terminal: will cost approximate the original purchase?
- Will additions impede network service? Can the operation tolerate out-of-service periods for growth?
- How must existing terminals or the media access controller be modified to accommodate new or disconnected terminals?
- Do you expect the nature of traffic to change for any planned or foreseeable reason?
- What are the penalties of response time delays?
- Can the network access mode, transmission medium, or topology be modified to accommodate growth if necessary?

REARRANGEMENT: THE OFFICE ENVIRONMENT

Many offices are in a continual state of transition. Desks, terminals and telephones are regularly moved as organizations realign and as data communications applications change. Industrial processes, on the other hand, are more stable. Once a local network is in place in a factory, it is likely to remain in place until some major realignment occurs.

Some types of local network are more adaptable to rearrangement than others. Circuit-switched networks with a star configuration are often wired to central distribution points and branched from there. Baseband and broadband networks can also be configured in a modified star topology where lines branch to terminals. With a star network, rearrangements can usually be accomplished at a central point.

Often the weight of the transmission medium is important because it may be necessary to place cable in suspended ceilings. When cable is being installed in buildings, the difficulty of maneuvering heavy cable reels may increase installation costs.

Frequency of rearrangement should be considered, not only in the selection of the network, but also in how it is laid out. If future changes are likely, they can be accomplished more easily if they are anticipated and incorporated into the plan. Questions you will want to consider include:

- How frequently is the organization likely to change its physical location?
- How costly are network rearrangements?
- How easily can the cable be tapped? Are there restrictions on how closely taps can be placed? Are these compatible with your rearrangement plans?
- Are major physical or software changes required to move stations?

VULNERABILITY TO SYSTEM OUTAGE

The IEEE 802 Committee has decided that a LAN should be invulnerable to the failure of a single element. Bus networks generally meet this specification. Token ring networks, where signals pass in series through all nodes, can suffer complete system outage from a single failed node unless they are designed to automatically bypass the failed component. In addition, switched networks are vulnerable to failure because their operation depends on the functioning of a single central controller. Some points to consider in evaluating vulnerability are:

- Does the network have a single central element? If so, is it protected with automatic switching or redundancy?
- Do all signals have to pass through a single element? If so, are provisions made for automatic bypass? If the element is bypassed, are the adjacent nodes still within signaling distance of each other?
- What is the mean time between failure and the mean time to repair of the total network?

- Is the technology mature enough that the predicted incidence of failure is accurate, or does it rely on unproven engineering estimates?
- How readily accessible are the vendor's repair forces?

NEED FOR OFF–NET COMMUNICATIONS

There is a wide difference among local network alternatives in the method and ease of implementing off-net communications. Circuit-switched local networks, particularly PBXs, are generally more adaptable to off-net communications over the telephone network than multiple access local networks, which require expensive gateways. For access to public data networks, most local networks require gateway circuitry that usually supports the X.25 protocols.

Communication between the local network and other private networks is yet another consideration. Organizations with an application load too large for one local network will split into two or more separate networks. In this case, internetwork communication will usually be required. Establish your requirements by considering the following:

- What percentage of communication will be off-net?
- What is the nature of off-net traffic? Is it bulk or bursty?
- What public networks must be accessed: data, telephone, or both?
- What types of private networks must be accessed: microwave, other local networks, PBXs, etc?
- What protocols are required? Is the network capable of supporting these protocols?
- What is the data speed requirement for your off-net communications?

COMPATIBILITY WITH MUTIPLE VENDORS

There are two schools of thought regarding compatibility when implementing local networks. One suggests that you should obtain your total requirements from one vendor. In that way, there is no question whose equipment is at fault when failures or incompatibilities occur. Finding technicians who can integrate multiple vendors' equipment is difficult at best and may be impractical for some applications. The main problem with this approach is that you are at the mercy of the vendor's pricing policies and ability to keep up with technology. When you lack alternatives, you lack the ability to bargain for a good price. However, the relationship between a vendor and yourself as a valued customer may be one that you want to preserve.

The other school of thought believes that the more nearly you can achieve universal compatibility, the more freedom you will have in choosing and applying equipment. If the vendor's performance is unsatisfactory, you can switch to another vendor for better performance and growth.

Both arguments have logic. Your choice will be a matter of your own experience and objectives. Major considerations included are:

- What kind of equipment is currently installed? Is it from a single vendor?
- Are there systems on the market to integrate your existing equipment into a local network, or will certain choices make your equipment obsolete?
- What is your relationship with perferred vendors? Are their prices consistently competitive?
- Does the vendor's track record convince you that long-term support is available?

INSTALLED BASE OF EQUIPMENT

Except for the few start-up users of data communications, most organizations have an equipment base and require that a local network be compatible with their existing equipment. Some questions to consider are:

- What protocols and physical interfaces does the network support? Are these compatible with existing equipment?
- Does the vendor offer the capability to mix or integrate various manufacturers' equipment?

- Will existing equipment be made obsolete by your choice of local network?
- Can this system use existing wiring?
- Does your organization have an existing PBX or other circuit-switched system? Does it have capacity to handle expected terminal growth?

NEED FOR OTHER COMMUNICATION MODES

All local networks are designed for data transmission, and with other factors being equal, the selection may boil down to how well the network meets your requirements for other forms of communication such as voice, video and facsimile. The most limited form of network in this respect is the base-band network, which can handle only data effectively. Circuit-switched networks, including all PBXs and, to a limited degree, data switches can handle voice communication with some sacrifice in data communication ability. Broadband networks are the most versatile. Most are designed to handle both video and data, and some can also support voice, although not economically. This versatility comes with some sacrifice in the cost of data transmissions alone.

This diversity of options suggests a searching, long-range analysis of your communications needs. Considerations include:

- Do you need video transmission? If so, does it parallel locations where data and voice communication are needed?
- How much off-net communication do you require? Is your voice traffic largely contained within the organization or is most of your business off-net?
- Have most of your voice and video requirements been accommodated, or have you reached the point where major additions or rearrangements are required?

EQUIPMENT AVAILABILITY

The amount of lead time the vendor requires before delivering the network components is a clue to several important considerations in selecting the network. If much lead time is required, it may indicate that the network is not fully developed. Of course, it can also indicate that the vendor can't meet a high demand for a product fast enough. If the network consists of components made by a variety of manufacturers, the availability of all components must be considered. Some typical considerations are:

- What is the interval from order to delivery? What is the manufacturer's record in meeting advertised intervals?
- Has the network been thoroughly tested in service or will you be acquiring an early model?
- What written performance guarantees is the vendor willing to give?
- How many systems are currently in service? What are the names, addresses, and telephone numbers of the users?

SECURITY REQUIREMENTS

In any kind of contention network, the potential of a security breach is always present. In broadcast transmissions typical of bus and ring topologies, a data signal is presented to all terminals. It is inevitable that messages will be intercepted by someone with sufficient motivation. However, if the transmitted information is not sensitive, no one will bother to tap the network. With circuit-switched networks, messages are not broadcast but directed to a single terminal, resulting in a better security system than to multiple access networks.

The transmission medium is an important element to security. Twisted-pair wire is easy to tap. Radio transmissions can be easily intercepted. Fiber optic cable is difficult to tap, and coaxial cable somewhere in between. You will want to consider these questions in evaluating security:

- What is the nature of the transmitted information? Could an unauthorized person have a motive for breaching security?
- If taps or other unauthorized access occur, how easily can they be detected?
- Does the application provide security? For example, can the data be encrypted?

FAULT ISOLATION CAPABILITY

When a network element or the total network fails, the more rapidly it can be restored to service, the more valuable the network. Some systems are equipped with internal diagnostics that aid in rapid trouble isolation and restoral. This is particularly true of circuit-switched networks, and can also be true of both contention and noncontention networks that are equipped for self-diagnosis.

You should also determine whether the network is inherently designed for fault isolation. For example, a ring network should be designed to identify which node has failed. It should be designed for bypass of a failed node, and the media access controller or network control center should provide alarms indicating a loss of received signal to aid in rapid fault isolation. Some factors you will want to consider are:

- What provisions have been made for automatic diagnosis of intermittent or failed conditions?
- Is the network designed for rapid trouble isolation?
- What kinds of alarms alert you to failures?
- Does the network provide a means for distinguishing between failures of the electronics and of the transmission medium?
- How well documented is the network? Are trouble-shooting manuals available? Are they written in lay terms, or do they require a trained service technician to understand them?

ABILITY TO GATHER TRAFFIC STATISTICS

From the local network's first design through the growth additions and periodic analysis of overloads, you will find a need for information about the character of traffic on your network. In fact, undoubtedly your first impediment to doing an accurate local network design will be the lack of statistical data from your existing terminals. Therefore, in selecting a local network you will find that the ability to collect such information is vital to managing the network.

While circuit-switched networks are usually sensitive to

the number of call attempts and to the holding time of the network, these networks can be blind to the character of the traffic. With a single connection, numerous packets or messages can be sent between terminals. Furthermore, the connection could be idle for long periods and not be apparent in traffic statistics unless the central switch has been programmed to detect such information.

Contention and noncontention networks can gather statistics in a higher order protocol. However, since the capability to gather statistical information is outside the constraints of network standards, you will want to consider the following:

- What kind of traffic data does the system provide? Does it provide enough information to enable you to evaluate the nature of your traffic? Can you determine which terminals originate and terminate most of the load?
- Does the network provide malfunction counts such as lost tokens, mutilated packets, and number of packets in error?
- Is statistical data available in mechanized form? Does the vendor provide any interpretive service to improve network effectiveness from the information collected?

RESPONSE TIME

An ideal local network should not impose response delays on the attached terminals. In some applications delay can be tolerated in exchange for reduced cost, but in other operations the cost of delays is so great that a low-cost network cannot be considered. The nature of your application must be studied in detail and carefully matched to the networks on the market. A contention network is most likely to introduce delays during busy peaks. Although this can happen with circuit-switched and token-passing networks, the delays can be distributed so that terminals receive equal access or some priority access, depending on the requirements of the user.

Delays can occur not only with terminal-to-terminal access, but also with terminals attempting access to shared devices such as a modem pool or gateway to a public data network. Delays into each of these ports are predictable and should be integrated into the network design. If the vendor provides a network modeling package, the effects of delays can be more readily foreseen than if you make manual calculations.

Another consideration closely related to response time is your requirement for data transfer speed. For example, to link two CPUs, a contention network would be a poor choice. If terminals require off-net access at 9600 b/s or more, most types of circuit-switched networks would be unsatisfactory because of their inherent speed limitations. Some questions for evaluating response time include:

- What are the penalties for response delays? If the network is busy, does the system queue users for later access without disrupting the application?
- Should some terminals be given higher priority than others?
- Does the vendor have a network modeling tool to simulate your application load on the network and to predict delays in response time or to peripheral devices and circuits?
- What is the effective network throughput in kb/s? How does this compare with your throughput requirements?
- When the network reaches maximum capacity, are delays evenly distributed to terminals? Is some throughput still possible during overload, or does the network begin to use maximum capacity in attending to internal functions such as collision recovery?
- What built-in overload protection does the network provide?
- What data transfer speed between devices does your application require? Is the network capable of meeting the requirement?

NETWORK DIAMETER

Distance limitations are an important factor in choosing a contention LAN. When the network diameter exceeds the design limitations of a contention network, a circuit-switched or token-passing network will be required, or the network will have to be segregated through a repeater. Sometimes, as an alternative, the network speed can be reduced, or a medium with higher propagation speed such as fiber optics can be used. Some of the main considerations are:

- What is the maximum distance between terminals in your application? How does this distance compare to the capability of the network?
- What transmission medium do you plan to use? If the distance is restrictive, can you change the transmission medium and solve the problem?
- What data rate is necessary to support your throughput requirements? Can the speed be reduced to accommodate a few outlying terminals?
- Can the network diameter be extended economically with repeaters or bridges?

DISTRIBUTION OF TERMINALS

In selecting a local network, not only is the distance between terminals or nodes important, but the distribution of terminals must also be considered. If terminals are sparsely spaced throughout the area, or if there are few terminals to connect, star networks tend to be economical. When the terminals are dense and clustered, bus networks are more feasible than they are with longer distances. If the terminals are clustered, you may want to consider access units that allow numerous terminals to be connected on a port contention basis. Some factors to consider are:

- Are your terminals clustered or widely dispersed throughout the network?
- How difficult is it to cable between terminals? Are there problems with right-of-way or with capacity in existing conduits?
- Is there sufficient capacity in existing cables?
- Is wiring already in place for a PBX or closed circuit television.

ENVIRONMENT

Environmental disturbances come from the possibility of physical damage, electrical disturbances, the weather, temperature changes, and the physical space available for installing the transmission medium. In some cases, only one type of local network may be feasible because of a requirement for the network to survive in a hostile physical environment or because of the application's physical limitations.

For example, in an industrial environment with sharp impulses of induced electrical current, the use of fiber optics may be required, narrowing your choices of network. Likewise, limited conduit space and the need for a large point-to-point circuit capacity may also mandate the use of fiber optics. It may be necessary for a node to exist in an area with wide temperature extremes (such as outdoors) or in an environmental testing chamber, in which case you must be certain the equipment can withstand the extremes. When direct burial of cable is needed, be sure the cable is so designed. Factors to consider are:

- Are there interfering electrical signals in any part of the cable route in your application?
- What is the likelihood of physical damage? Is it necessary to place the cable in conduit? Is there space available?
- Are there extreme environmental conditions in which the network must survive? What is the operating temperature range of the equipment?
- Is the network subject to physical shock or interference from electrical devices in the environment?

CHANGING TOPOLOGIES OR TRANSMISSION MODES

Occasionally, it is advantageous to change topology or transmission mode. For example, an organization outgrowing a bus contention network may choose to convert to a token ring. In this case, it is best to avoid rewiring the network. Some networks support conversions from baseband to broadband and this can be an attractive factor for some applications. At some point in the future you may also need to increase the transmission speed. This requirement would eliminate certain low bandwidth alternatives. Consider the following:

- What will be the ultimate size and capacity of your network?
- How do you plan to expand the network when it outgrows its current capacity?
- What is the ultimate transmission speed you plan for the network?
- How do you plan to increase transmission speed over the current capacity?

TRANSITION METHODS

If the transition from an existing to a new system will be gradual—adding terminals one or two at a time—the risk of network overload is small; and uncertainties in calculating your traffic load and characteristics can probably be absorbed by the network. If conversion is likely to be sudden, and your traffic load is unknown or crowding the capacity of a contention network, you may decide a deterministic system such as token passing offers the least risk. Even though delayed response time is inherent with a deterministic system, delay is uniform, and each node is assured of its share of network capacity. Questions to consider include:

- Is the nature of your traffic bulk or bursty?
- How much spare capacity does a particular alternative offer?
- Are you adding several terminals to the network at once, or is the transition gradual?
- What are the consequences of an overloaded network that must be deloaded after it is installed?
- How thoroughly has your data traffic load been studied? How much confidence do you have in the results?

COST

Few organizations purchase a local network without a careful check on the price tag. Not only is the cost of the network critical, but you must also consider the cost of deferring the purchase entirely. When you are satisfied that the purchase is economically justified (a process we look at closely in Chapter 16) the costs of the alternatives offered on the market deserve comparison.

Cost comparisons made strictly on the basis of the manufacturers' price lists are not reliable because there are other cost factors to consider. The initial comparisons should be made on the basis of total installed costs including the price of the hardware, software, design engineering, shipping, installation, and initialization. The equipment costs should include all the elements needed to get the system operational, including costs of interface units, cabling, terminal software, training, and other such one-time charges.

Perhaps even more important are the recurring costs throughout the service life of the network: hardware maintenance, software maintenance, costs of growth additions, and projected costs of down time including lost labor. Such costs should be compared on a life cycle basis to derive a realistic comparison among the alternatives. Life cycle costs can be approximated with a spreadsheet program such as VisiCalc™, Lotus 1, 2, 3™, or Multiplan™ and other popular spreadsheet programs. The method is outlined in Appendix B.

Another consideration is the potential for future cost reductions. By nature, some technologies offer more potential for future cost reductions than others. For example, much of the access logic in a standard baseband contention network can be encapsulated in a chip. As sales volumes increase the chip price will come down and future additions will be less expensive. Broadband local networks, on the other hand, use mature CATV technology, which is analog and less subject to the benefits of large scale integration. Much of the cost reduction potential has already been realized because of the large quantities of equipment that have been purchased by CATV companies. This is not to say that future cost reductions are unlikely, but the magnitude is likely to be less than with digital techniques.

In comparing costs of local network alternatives, consider the following factors:

- What will installation cost compared to alternative networks?
- What recurring costs do you expect throughout the life of the network?
- What is the manufacturer's charge policy for upgrades? Is there an annual maintenance or user's fee?
- Will the network support your existing equipment, or is the purchase of new equipment required?
- What is the cost of growth additions?
- How long do you expect the system to survive? Will it have a shortened service life because of early obsolescence or because it cannot meet your capacity requirements?
- Does the network require an investment in specialized test equipment that you would not otherwise need?
- How much does it cost to train a new operator?
- What is the expected failure rate of the network? What are the down-time costs to your organization? How much will it cost to repair?
- Does the technology offer potential for future cost reductions?

SUMMARY

While the questions raised in this chapter are not to be interpreted as requirements, they are intended to provoke thought. In Chapter 16 we will build on the information we have developed in this chapter and will suggest a process for matching your requirements to the characteristics of the equipment the market offers.

16

Selecting a Local Network

In a market that offers so many alternatives, selecting the best local network for your application can be a formidable task. In this chapter we will discuss a process that will narrow the choices. Here are the steps.

1. Collect information on the alternatives.
2. Develop a list of requirements.
3. Send requests for quotations to vendors capable of meeting your requirements.
4. Evaluate life cycle costs.
5. Select the best system.
6. Select the best vendor.

The process isn't as mechanical as this list implies because the steps don't sequence themselves neatly. Instead, some part of each step is likely to be going on throughout the selection process, but we'll discuss the steps as if they behaved in this order.

COLLECT INFORMATION ON THE ALTERNATIVES

Trade magazines are full of advertisements about local networks. If you aren't in a hurry, you can collect information by circling blocks on reader cards. Unfortunately, the information is rarely more detailed than the advertisements, and the replies will trickle in slowly.

Trade shows provide an opportunity to inspect the equipment and talk to manufacturers' representatives. However, some excellent products will not be represented at the trade shows because many manufacturers do not attend them all. Trade shows do offer an excellent way to see and compare many products in a short time, and the seminars and technical sessions are often a valuable source of information.

If you can be specific about your requirements, a phone call or letter to a manufacturer will bring detailed product information, or you may choose to send a more formal Request for Information (RFI) letter. The more specific you can be, the less likely you will be inundated with product information unrelated to your requirements.

The most productive although time-consuming method of gathering information is by attending vendor-supported product presentations. Product representatives can provide you with a great deal of information about both vendors and competing products. You will find this a fruitful and inexpensive education on what competitors have to offer. The face-to-face interaction gives you an opportunity to ask questions that will help with one of the most difficult parts of the process— understanding your own requirements.

DEVELOP A LIST OF REQUIREMENTS

After gathering information from vendors, following the suggestions in the last chapter, and analyzing the data communications needs of the users in your organization, you are ready to develop a detailed list of requirements. In their excellent book *The Rational Manager*, Kepner and Tregoe recommend dividing requirements into two classes, mandatory and desirable. This aids in rapidly screening products because those that fail to meet the mandatory list are rejected at the outset. By narrowing your focus you can give detailed attention to the surviving products.

Desirable features should be ranked or grouped into a range from highly desirable to desirable but not essential. This process is an excellent aid to your thinking because while you are ranking features, you are evaluating your requirements in detail at the same time.

Unless you have already done so, you should also survey the data communications needs of the users in your organization. Although you can get by without detailed usage information during the preliminary product search, the information will be needed at the detailed-design stage. The more you know about the character of your data traffic, the more accurately you can fit the local network alternatives to your requirements. Figure 16.1 is a form that is adaptable to your organization. The form can be used for conducting an interview in each organizational unit to collect information about the nature of internal data communications.

From your knowledge of the organization, you can provide the details that affect the choice of alternatives, such as distance between terminals, restrictions to placing cabling, and evaluations of existing equipment such as PBXs. The decision chart in Table 16.1 is an aid to narrowing the choices. For example, if your application is unable to tolerate delays in response, you will probably discard CSMA/CD as an alternative. This chart compares the alternatives for topology, access method, transmission medium and modulation method. The alternative that is generally the most favorable is shown on the left, ranging to the least favorable on the right.

REQUESTS FOR QUOTATIONS

A request for quotations (RFQ) to vendors is a means of further narrowing the choices. Most essential is that you prepare a detailed list of requirements from the information you have collected to this point. List mandatory features as requirements. List desirable features in the order of their importance.

The elimination process begins. From the list of mandatory features, it becomes evident that some vendors are not

Company _____ Division _____ Date _____

Data Terminals (Use separate form for each device)

Mfgr. _____ Synchronous ☐ Protocol _____

Model _____ Asynchronous ☐ Data Rate _____

Application _____

Messages Sent Per Day:

Average _____ Minimum _____ Maximum _____

Message Block Size:

Average _____ Minimum _____ Maximum _____

Messages Received Per Day:

Average _____ Minimum _____ Maximum _____

Words Per Message:

Average _____ Minimum _____ Maximum _____

Terminals Communicated With: _____

_____

_____

Peak Traffic:

Day of Week _____ Time of Day _____ Season _____

Is information above based on actual data? ☐ Estimated data? ☐

Are any new applications planned? _____ If so, describe

_____

_____

What is the estimate of growth in this application?

Two years _____

Five years _____

How much outage time can be tolerated? _____

FIGURE 16.1 Sample form for collecting local data transmission requirements

TABLE 16.1 Decision Chart—Comparison of Alternatives vs. Requirements

Most Favorable → Least Favorable

Factor	Topology	Access Method	Transmission Medium	Modulation Method
Security	Star Bus Ring	Switched CSMA/CD Token	Fiber Coax Twisted pair	Little effect
Data Rate	Little effect	Token CSMA/CD Switched	Fiber Coax Twisted pair	Little effect
Response Time	Little effect	Token CSMA/CD Switched	Little effect	Little effect
Network Diameter	Star Bus Ring	Switched Token CSMA/CD	Fiber Coax Twisted pair	Broadband Baseband
Cost	Bus Ring Star	CSMA/CD Token Switched	Twisted pair Coax Fiber	Baseband Broadband
Ease of Growth	Bus Star Ring	CSMA/CD Switched Token	Fiber Coax Twisted pair	Broadband Baseband
Ease of Rearrangement	Star Bus Ring	Switched Token CSMA/CD	Twisted pair Coax Fiber	Baseband Broadband
Vulnerability to Outage	Bus Star Ring	CSMA/CD Token Switched	Fiber Coax Twisted pair	Baseband Broadband
Off-Net Communications	Star Ring Bus	Switched Token CSMA/CD	Little effect	Little effect
Compatibility with Multiple Terminals	Little effect	Switched Token CSMA/CD	Little effect	Little effect
Capacity	Little effect	Little effect	Fiber Coax Twisted pair	Broadband Baseband

capable of meeting your system requirements. These are eliminated. For example, a users' survey may reveal peak traffic loads not supported by CSMA/CD. If the organization has a PBX satisfactory for voice traffic but unable to support the additional load imposed by data, both CSMA/CD and the PBX system can be eliminated from consideration. On this basis, the RFQ will be sent only to vendors of token networks.

Send an RFQ and a cover letter to prospective vendors. The RFQ outlines the terms and conditions for doing business with the vendor. The letter should make it clear that the selection of a system will not be made on price alone. Include the following points in the letter or the requirements list:

- The vendor's cutoff date for responding.
- The names and addresses of other users.
- Detailed technical information about the system.
- A summary of the factors that will influence your decision to purchase.
- A disclaimer that allows you to reject any or all responses.
- A summary of important negotiable terms in the purchase contract: warranty, delivery terms, requirement for technical support, and other such features you require to ensure satisfactory performance.
- A summary of services required in addition to the furnishing of equipment: system design, traffic load analysis, training, installation, a maintenance contract, and any other services not available to you from other sources.
- Information on costs incurred from administering the system: its expected failure rate and the costs of future expansion.
- A list of the equipment and external networks with which the system must be compatible.

EVALUATE LIFE CYCLE COSTS

After receiving the responses to the RFQ, you may find that only one network meets the requirements. If so, the decision is easy—either buy that system or keep what you have. Rarely, however, are the alternatives so limited. The problem more likely will be which of numerous attractive alternatives to buy.

Remember that the best product isn't necessarily the one with the lowest price. The initial price is paid once. The rest of the costs continue long after the technicians have packed their cable coring tools and their time domain reflectometers, and have gone home. The task is to find out which alternative extracts the least amount of cash from your bank account from the time you acquire the local network until you discard it. The best way to select among alternatives is to use a process known as a life cycle study.

LIFE CYCLE ANALYSIS

The life cycle analysis technique is widely used by purchasing agents and engineers to choose the least costly of a series of alternatives. The techniques are explained in detail in any good financial text, but they usually won't be described as a life cycle study. These studies may come under another name, such as discounted cash flow analysis, but life cycle analysis uses the same financial tools. We will discuss the techniques in this section, and will show you in Appendix B how to apply them. From this discussion, anyone with a financial or engineering economics background should be able to apply the techniques with the help of someone who understands local network technology.

TIME VALUE OF MONEY

Money invested over a period of time yields a return if the investment is economically sound. The objective of investing in a local network is to obtain a satisfactory return on the resources invested in the network. Unless the investment yields more than the alternative of leaving things as they are, the investment is economically unsound. Of course some kind of operational requirement may make the investment mandatory, but you still must determine which alternative is the most economically efficient. To do this, we will use a financial factor, net present value (NPV) to evaluate the alternatives.

NPV is the discounted sum of all the cash flows from owning a product—from the time of its purchase until it is retired from service. To determine NPV, you must first identify the magnitude and duration of every cash flow both into and away from the organization, then discount the cash flows to their present value (by a discount table, computer program, or mechanized spread sheet), and finally, add them together. If the NPV is positive, the investment returns money to the organization. If the NPV is negative, the investment is a consumer of capital.

The process of discounting sometimes confuses nonfinancial people, so a brief explanation is in order. Compounding is a factor that is understood by nearly everyone, and because it is the opposite of discounting, it will help explain the concept. If a sum of money is invested at a given rate of interest for a period of time, compounding determines the magnitude of the investment at the end of the period. To compound for a period, you multiply the starting investment by the interest rate and add the result to the investment at the end of the period. The end-of-period investment becomes the starting investment for the next period. The process works in this way:

Start of Period Investment		Interest Rate		Initial Investment		End of Period Investment
	×		+		=	
$1.00		10%		$1.00		$1.10
1.10		10%		1.10		1.21
1.21		10%		1.21		1.32

You determine compound or future value by applying a table or a simple mathematical formula. An abbreviated table of compound interest and present value at 10 percent is shown in Table 16.2. Compound interest and present worth tables can be found in any good financial text.

The effect of discounting is the reverse of compounding. When you are given an amount of money at some time in the future and want to know how much that future investment is worth at present, the value can be obtained from a current value table. For example, suppose we must make a $10,000 addition to a local network five years from now, and the cost of money is 10 percent. By applying the discount or present value factor for five years at 10 percent (.6209), we can determine that the present value of that investment is $10,000 × .6209 or $6,209. To look at it another way, if you put $6,209 in

TABLE 16.2 Compound and Present Value of $1

Year	Compound Value of $1 at 10%	Present Value of $1 at 10%
1	1.00	.9091
2	1.10	.8264
3	1.21	.7513
4	1.33	.683
5	1.46	.6209

the bank today at 10 percent, you would have $10,000 in five years.

You should not make a financial decision on the basis of NPV alone. There are many other financial indicators to consider. Key indicators include internal rate of return (IRR) and present worth of expenditures (PWE). For the sake of simplicity, we will use only NPV because it is easy to calculate. Appendix B shows how to calculate NPV using a spread sheet program. Also you can use a simple BASIC program, such as the one included in *Automating Your Office: How to Do It, How to Justify It* (Green, 1984, p. 224), can be used to compute NPV with little effort.

A life cycle study is the process of estimating all the cash flows related to product alternatives, determining the economic indicators of each product, and selecting the one that most nearly achieves your financial objectives. The product with the highest NPV will normally be the best buy, although constraints on your investment capital may mandate the use of an alternative with an initial cost lower than the one with the highest NPV.

LIFE CYCLE FACTORS

The first step in a life cycle study is to estimate all the cash flows for each of the major expenditures required during the life of a product. Once these are arrayed into a spread sheet (as in Appendix B) or entered in a program, calculating NPV is simple. However, getting functional figures is not that easy. You will need to estimate and include in the study some major factors:

Capital and other one-time charges

- Equipment cost including shipping
- Network design and engineering
- Installation (including costs of supporting fixtures such as conduit)
- Software
- Transition costs from existing system
- Costs from required hardware and software changes
- Growth additions
- Salvage value

Recurring Costs

- Hardware maintenance (costs of locating and repairing trouble, discounted for free repairs during warranty).
- Software maintenance or other recurring fees.
- Lost work time and other down-time costs.

Many of the above costs, such as maintenance, are difficult to predict. One way of anticipating maintenance costs is to talk with users of similar systems. Without documented experience, you will have to use the manufacturer's calculated mean time between failure rate to estimate how frequently repairs will be necessitated.

Other factors such as salvage value, which is a positive cash flow at the end of the service life, can be estimated within a reasonable range of accuracy. Often, the best estimate of such factors is the figure you would use for tax purposes in calculating depreciation.

A fundamental rule to follow in life cycle analysis is to disregard cash flows that are equal among all competing products. The result you are after is the difference between products, not the absolute value. If there is no difference among cash flows for one of the factors, it can safely be omitted without affecting the outcome of the study.

Life cycle study factors must be chosen with care if the study is to have validity. The discount rate is an important factor to choose. It has no effect on the initial investment because cash flows during the first year are not discounted, but in subsequent years the discount rate can have a significant effect. The higher the discount rate, the lower the NPV, and therefore the less effect a cash flow has on the decision.

Because capital investments occur at the beginning of a project, and recurring cash flows continue throughout a project's life, a large initial capital investment may eventually be offset by savings in recurring costs. For example, one network might have a low initial cost, but the savings might be more than offset by the costs of maintenance and lost production time. The life cycle analysis is designed to quantify these differences.

Service life has a significant effect on the decision. Assume that two products are being considered and one is higher in initial cost, but lower in annual costs. The higher-priced product has to remain in service long enough to amortize its greater initial cost. The shorter the service life, the less opportunity a product has to offset an initial cost disadvantage. Therefore, the estimated service life used in a life cycle analysis is important. A good rule of thumb is to use the service life allowed by the IRS for tax purposes as the study life in a life cycle analysis.

A full discussion of life cycle analysis is a topic varied enough to fill a volume itself and is beyond the scope of this book. If your organization does not possess the expertise to evaluate the life cycle performance of products, you will find it worthwhile to develop the expertise or engage outside assistance. The risk of buying a product on the basis of initial cost alone is too great. You cannot afford to ignore the greater precision of a life cycle analysis.

SELECT THE BEST SYSTEM

Often, a product cannot be selected on the basis of economics alone. In addition to life cycle costs there are several other factors to consider.

STATE OF PRODUCT DEVELOPMENT

There is an optimum buying time in the product life cycle: the product has been thoroughly tested in the field but is far from being discontinued. Don't expect an easy guide to unde-

veloped or soon-to-be-obsolescent products. It is something
you must estimate from a knowledge of the technology and
hints from vendors. Just remember that new isn't necessarily
superior. Even the best vendors have inflicted their dogs on
the market.

DEGREE OF UNKNOWN FACTORS IN
THE SELECTION EQUATION

A life cycle study will always yield the mathematically correct answer. There is no magic about it; it has been designed
to do exactly that based on accurate input assumptions. The
problem is that about the only thing you can rely on is the networks installed cost, and that, only if you have an airtight contract. The rest has some degree of variability, and the problem
is to determine how much. The best way to assess variability is
to rerun the life cycle analysis with different input assumptions. If the product remains the winner no matter what the
assumptions, you can be reasonably sure you have chosen the
right one.

SELECT THE BEST VENDOR

In implementing a technology as new and relatively un-
tested as local networks, the choice of vendor may have a
greater effect on the success of the system than the product
itself. If only one vendor can provide the support you need to
design, implement, and maintain the network, it will be difficult to justify choosing another system, even if it appears
superior. In most localities, several choices are available.
However, distinguishing among the choices is not easy. In this
section we will discuss some of the factors you should consider in evaluating a vendor.

MAINTENANCE SUPPORT

Even though the reliability of modern electronic equipment is high with calculated mean time between failures of
several months or even years, in the event the system is down
you will need immediate and competent assistance. Whether

the local network is supporting an industrial process, a distributed data processing application, or office automation, down-time costs will escalate rapidly. The more the work force or the process depends on the local network, the more urgent the need to restore a failed system as quickly as possible.

You should ask the following questions concerning the vendor's capabilities:

- What is the driving time between your premises and the vendor's?
- How many technicians does the vendor employ? Are there enough people to cover vacations, resignations, and absences, or does the vendor have to import help from another branch in such cases?
- Is specialized test equipment needed to locate faults? If so, does the vendor have it available on site?
- What training is required to maintain the system? Have the vendor's service forces been trained?
- How many accounts does each technician service?
- Are the technicians local network specialists, or do they maintain other equipment as well?
- Is technical assistance available during your scheduled working hours and work week?
- Does the vendor charge for out-of-hours maintenance? Is the charge reasonable?
- Is a maintenance contract available? Is it economical?

IMPLEMENTATION AND INSTALLATION ASSISTANCE

Although some users will install their own local network, the skills needed for installation are specialized enough that most organizations will use outside forces for the job. The simplest networks, such as baseband twisted pair, can be installed with low-skill labor. However, coaxial or fiber optic cables require specialized tools and test equipment for installation and testing; also trained technicians may be needed to debug the network.

In deciding whether to install the network yourself or have the vendor install it, you will want to consider the following:

- What skill levels are needed to install and test the network? Are these skills readily available on the labor market?
- Are specialized tools and test equipment needed? Can they be rented? Will the vendor supply them?
- What is your cost estimate for installation? How does it compare to the vendor's installation price?
- Are the installation and testing instructions well-documented?
- Does your locality require a license for cable installations?
- What building or fire codes may restrict the type of cabling? Will special jacketing such as Teflon or conduit be required?

DESIGN SUPPORT

As with installation, most users will have the vendor design the network instead of attempting to do it themselves. Network design requires specialized skills, and perhaps mechanized modeling tools and network design software. Sometimes design assistance is included in the purchase price or is offered by the vendor as an inducement to buy. These are some considerations in evaluating the vendor's design capabilities:

- Is specialized knowledge needed to design and lay out the network? For example, are amplifier, tap, and branching filter placement critical?
- Does the vendor provide design assistance or training for your forces?
- What does the vendor charge for designing compared to costs from internal sources?
- Is contract design available on the market?
- How severe are the consequences of overdesign or underdesign? For example, if you design with excess capacity, will future growth take care of the excess?
- Are computer programs or other design aids available? Is it feasible to design the network without them?
- Is the design process documented in a step-by-step procedure comprehensible to an untrained person?
- Is the vendor capable of evaluating your traffic load?

NETWORK MODELING CAPABILITY

Given the traffic characteristics of your application, many vendors are capable of simulating the network operation with a computer program that can include all the variables that affect network operation. Although this is not an absolute requirement for selecting a vendor, the capability of modeling your network should lend validity to the design. If the network throughput deteriorates, or if you add more terminals, the modeling equation should help determine the effect of increasing data speed or adding/removing load.

INTEGRATION CAPABILITIES

Most network components are not available within a single network package. It may be necessary to purchase cable from one vendor, media access units from another vendor, and terminals from a third. Someone will ultimately be responsible for ensuring that these components work as an integrated whole. If one of the vendors does not assume this responsibility, you will be the ultimate system integrator. Unless you are prepared to accept this role, you may want to select a vendor who is prepared to warrant total system performance.

Most local networks must be integrated with existing applications programs and face the problem of interfacing with hardware of diverse manufacture. For example, suppose you have a cluster of existing word processors with communications capabilities that have never been integrated into a network. Your plans call for adding a group of new word processors made by a different manufacturer and using different protocols. A centralized file shared by all word processors is also being added, and the network requires off-net communication to a distant group of word processors.

In such a network, the selection of the vendor will require not only the product that has off-net and protocol conversion capability, but may involve a vendor that knows how to implement such a network and integrate the products into a functioning unit. Think about the following considerations:

- What experience has the vendor had in system integration? What have been the results? Can the results be demonstrated or documented?

- Does the vendor have a staff of software engineers available for such work?
- What will system integration cost? How long will it take?
- If the vendor does not offer integration, who will assume overall responsibility for system performance?

STANDARDIZATION

Network standards are not necessary for all applications. However, purchase of a network that meets an IEEE standard is one way of obtaining compatibility with future terminal equipment purchases and avoiding obsolescence. Gateway circuits to other networks must meet the standards required by the network provider. For example, if you plan to communicate over the telephone network, the system must be capable of recognizing busy tone, dial tone, reorder, and other call progress signals. If you plan to communicate over a public data network such as Tymnet or Telenet, your network should be capable of an X.25 interface that is certified compatible with the data network. Some considerations are:

- What standards does the network meet? Are these compatible with your plans and requirements?
- What is the vendor's commitment to keeping the network current with changing standards?
- How important are standards in your operation?
- Has the network been certified for connection to public networks?

VENDOR EXPERIENCE

Local network technology is on the upward slope of the development curve. Although you can't tell it from the advertisements, many of the systems being touted by the vendors are still in the developmental state and have been tried only in test situations.

The risks in selecting an undeveloped system are high. You may wait months for delivery, may find the software has not been thoroughly debugged, and may spend time out of service while the vendor debugs problems that didn't occur in previous installations. On the other hand, buying a new system is some assurance against obsolescence, particularly if you choose a standard technology. The ideal situation is to choose the product just at the time it has been thoroughly debugged, but hasn't been on the market long enough to soon approach obsolescence. However, this state may not be easy to detect.

It is also advisable to evaluate the experiences of other users. Some questions to ask in evaluating experience are:

- How many users have applied this local network? Will the vendor give you names? What has been the users' experience?
- How new is the technology? Has the technology been thoroughly proven?
- Does the local network meet a recognized standard?
- How readily available is technical assistance in case of trouble?

PERFORMANCE GUARANTEES

Aside from reputation it is difficult to determine the vendor's degree of commitment to product support. A good way of ensuring performance is with a written guarantee that the vendor will either make the product work as specified or will remove it and refund your money. This warranty of performance is one reason for having the vendor design and install the system. If another vendor does the design and/or the installation, it may be questionable as to who is at fault should the system fail. Some considerations are:

- Will the vendor give performance guarantees? What kind of backing does the vendor give to the performance guarantee? (A performance bond is best.)
- What is the vendor's standard guarantee? Is it a true performance guarantee or merely a guarantee against manufacturing defects?
- Will the vendor refund installation and design costs if the equipment fails to function properly?

NEGOTIATE THE PURCHASE

With a new technology such as local networks, it is worthwhile negotiating a purchase contract, particularly if the manufacturer's representative has made certain affirmations that are not included in the standard warranty terms. Most warranties contain a statement that disclaims any warranty not expressly included. Your objective in purchasing a local network is to be certain that it meets your data transmission requirements. Therefore, you should insist on some guarantee of performance from the manufacturer. If the system doesn't perform to your expectations, the manufacturer should agree to fix it or replace it. If the system proves incompatible with your existing equipment or application, and the vendor has stated that it will be compatible, it is well to have a contract that places the responsibility for the remedy on the vendor.

The contract need not be legalistic and detailed. A letter of agreement is usually enough to set forth the responsibilities of both you and the vendor for making the system function. Legal assistance at this stage of the negotiations is usually necessary.

SUMMARY

The local network thicket is dense and thorny. Little practical experience is available to help you assess the market, and blunders can be expensive. However, the rewards of improved productivity or reduced process cost are enough motivation to make the venture worthwhile for many organizations.

The admonition cannot be stated too frequently: know and thoroughly understand your requirements, both near and long term, and select the system that matches them most accurately. These last two chapters have recommended a process to follow, and though the process is not easy to apply and far from infallible, it is better than unaided impulse and intuition.

17

The Future of Local Networks

Local networks, like their metropolitan and global counterparts, are changing dramatically. In the past, choices were limited largely to services offered under tariff by telephone companies. Except for the largest organizations, networks were obtained from a monopoly carrier under rates and technical parameters prescribed by regulatory agencies. Now, with deregulation, a multitude of choices are emerging, and users can customize their communications services to meet their unique needs.

Over the past fifteen years, private network ownership has become increasingly attractive, especially with the demise of tariffs that restricted the interconnection of equipment not owned by the telephone companies. Although deregulation is probably the most powerful of the forces, numerous other changes are coming about that will alter the shape of communications drastically in coming years. The technology is advancing so rapidly that it is risky to predict what will happen to telecommunications. The information in this chapter is not, therefore, a prediction, but rather a synopsis of developments underway and an analysis of their probable effects on local networks.

TELECOMMUNICATIONS REGULATION

The time of limiting users to selecting telecommunications services from the tariff-based telephone company with rates monitored by regulatory commissions has passed. Regulation still exists in two of the three types of networks, global and metropolitan, but that is changing rapidly. Although current metropolitan networks are largely regulated, local networks are totally unregulated. and global networks are evolving toward eventual deregulation.

Telecommunications regulation is incompatible with the multiple option networks that are developing, and we can only hope for its demise within the next few years. At the time of this writing, the telecommunications industry in the United States is undergoing a drastic transformation. With a change of this magnitude, there is concern about its effects on consumers who have previously enjoyed subsidized local telephone rates. There is grave concern that without subsidies many people will be unable to afford local telephone service in the future.

Despite the turmoil of deregulation, the consumer should benefit in the long run. It is clear that we are now entering a new information age. Although it is difficult to foresee the effects on the average household, the information era will require facilities to transport quantities of information rapidly and economically regardless of their destination. It is also clear that information can now be transported most economically in digital form regardless of its source—that is, text, data, voice, or video. It is also clear that evolving into an all-digital network will require substantial investments in new equipment and facilities, and this investment will not occur quickly with regulated telecommunications and subsidized rates. It is not yet clear that the cost will be affordable to everyone, but the technology is on the horizon. Historically, technology has brought improved services within the price range of the masses.

The businesses and regulatory agencies that have the courage to dismantle the present structure in favor of the future should be encouraged because the emerging networks will lead us into the twenty-first century. The technology of the past is obsolete and must give way to the new.

THE SHAPE OF FUTURE NETWORKS

Throughout history, telephone networks have evolved in a linear fashion. Engineers have calculated the volume of traffic between major points and have constructed circuit highways to accommodate it. Switching systems have been linked in a hierarchical fashion to form countless circuits between end points. This vast system now resembles a gigantic time-shared computer that is controlled over millions of distributed ports with a very simple input/output device—the ordinary telephone.

In contrast to this linear, hierarchical, circuit-switched network, the network of the future can best be described as a flow. Much like flowing rivulets caused by the force of water over a mound of soil, the network of the future will be flowing rivulets of information—each rivulet boosed toward its destination by the force of the network, each identified by its individual address.

This is not to forecast the demise of the circuit-switched telephone network because circuit switching is an efficient way to handle voice as well as some data traffic. Rather than replace the telephone network, multiple networks will evolve from it to match the nature of the traffic they are intended to carry. Some data is distinctly for local application, some for metropolitan application, and some for long-haul application. For example, intraoffice electronic mail is principally local, communications between a point-of-sale terminal and a computer located in the same city is a metropolitan application, while an airline reservation system may span the globe.

While each network has its own domain and unique protocols, and while a great deal of the data flow is within that network itself, there is still a significant demand for communication between the domains. In the future, the user will be able to launch a message from a terminal and let the network ensure delivery. This is in contrast to today's network where the user is concerned with routing, translating addresses, terminal and protocol compatibility, and message integrity.

Narrowing the focus to local networks, it is clear that to apply many of the available options will require specialized knowledge, but the goal remains the same: The user should be required to understand the application, but not how the network itself functions. Communications should be as universally understood as driving a car. Just as a licensed driver can function effectively in any country that adheres to acknowledged rules of the road, users will ideally be able to communicate over networks in the future without concern for their protocols.

DIGITAL CONNECTIVITY IN THE
METROPOLITAN NETWORK

The main distinguishing feature in the network of the future will be the gradual evolution toward end-to-end digital connections. As we have seen in this book, analog transmission is rapidly disappearing in the local network. For the short distances involved, it is too cumbersome and too costly to convert digital signals to analog and back to digital again. When we leave the local network, however, it is very difficult to avoid analog transmission: The overwhelming bulk of existing circuitry is still analog.

In the metropolitan network, nearly all electronic switching machines installed before 1980 were analog for two practical reasons. First, the art of large-scale component integration had not progressed to the point that digital switching was economical. Equally important, nearly all local distribution facilities consist of twisted-pair cable. Although the cable can handle digital data within a limited range, the network has been designed for the inexpensive and ubiquitous analog telephone set, and there is not as yet an inexpensive digital replacement.

Several trends make it inevitable that metropolitan networks will evolve into a fully digital architecture. One of the important driving forces is the availability of digital switching systems. In time, digital switching will replace the older analog switching systems, but billions of dollars of investment will be needed, and the transition will take many years.

An equally important motivation is the development of metropolitan network standards. The analog telephone network was designed for ordinary telephone transmission by the Bell System to its own standards. The future network, however, will be designed to international standards with digital data transmission equally as important as voice. The CCITT has been working for several years on standards for the integrated services digital network (ISDN). Although the shape of this network is gradually emerging as a result of input from many diverse interests, the final design has not yet been adopted.

Another factor that will help advance multiple options for local data transport is the current activity of the IEEE 802 Committee to prepare and adopt metropolitan network standards. Numerous proprietary methods are on the market, but as yet, none has been adopted.

COMPETITION IN METROPOLITAN NETWORKS

Although local telephone distribution has been a regulated noncompetitive service in the past, competition for metropolitan data transport is beginning to develop from cable television companies as metropolitan areas are being wired for CATV. Although the basic CATV cable is a one-way system, many heavy-usage areas are installing dual cables that can offer videotex services and point-to-point data transmission services for commercial customers. Competition between the telephone companies and CATV companies is likely to become intense, resulting in a wide variety of alternatives vying for the market.

In response to competition and in an effort to participate in the lucrative data transmission markets, several new services are becoming available to replace traditional analog circuits and modems. Although these services are primarily offered by the Bell Operating Companies, equivalent services can be expected from other carriers in response to competition.

LOCAL AREA DATA TRANSPORT

Local Area Data Transport (LADT) is a metropolitan packet-switched network that was first introduced in some Bell Operating Companies in 1983 and will become more widely available in subsequent years. LADT is intended to overcome the drawbacks of circuit switching for metropolitan area data transmission.

With LADT, which is illustrated in Figure 17.1, users have

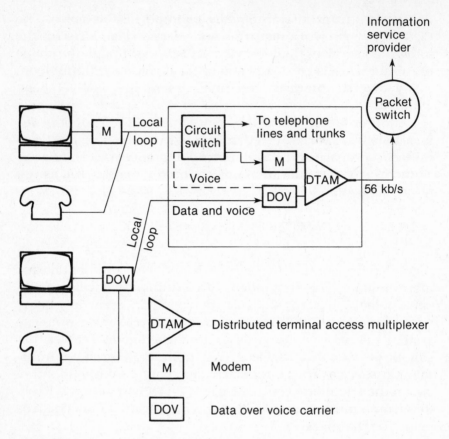

FIGURE 17.1   Local area data transport

access to a packet network through a statistical multiplexer called a distributed terminal access multiplexer (DTAM). The DTAM is accessed over a dialed-up connection for light users, or over a dedicated connection for heavy users. The dial-up user must be equipped with a 1200 baud 212A-compatible modem. The dedicated connection can be over a 4800 b/s circuit furnished by a data-over-voice carrier, or a 9.6 kb/s or 56 kb/s connection over a digital line.

CIRCUIT-SWITCHED DIGITAL CAPABILITY

Circuit-switched digital capability (CSDC) is a 56 kb/s intercity switched service that is being offered by some Bell companies and AT&T Communications, Inc. CSDC operates between local and long distance switching offices over full-duplex 56 kb/s lines, as shown in Figure 17.2. Between the subscriber and the local central office the circuit operates on an alternate voice/data basis over a two-wire circuit in a full-duplex mode. A special line circuit is required in the central office, and special terminating equipment on the user's premises.

The full-duplex mode is accomplished over the two-wire local loop by a technique known as **time compression multiplexing** (TCM). In TCM the network channel terminating equipment at the user's location and the line equipment in the central office operate in a 144 kb/s burst or ping-pong™ mode. The two terminals send at 56 kb/s, and the line is rapidly reversed by the terminating equipment. Because the TCM equipment is capable of operating more than twice the speed of the input signals, the users have the equivalent of a four-wire full-duplex circuit over the two-wire local loop.

INTEGRATED SERVICES DIGITAL NETWORK

Both LADT and CSDC and equivalent services are interim steps toward a totally new form of network, the ISDN. The ISDN is an attempt to introduce nonproprietary international standards into the future network. Currently, networks in all

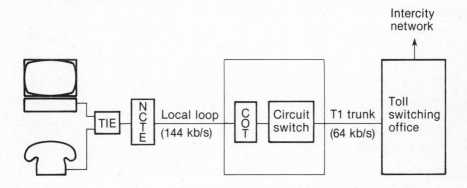

TIE   Terminal interface equipment
NCTE   Network channel terminating equipment
COT   Central office terminal

FIGURE 17.2   Circuit switched digital capability

countries have evolved from the manufacturers' proprietary standards or from standards set by each nation's Postal, Telephone, and Telegraph agencies. With the ISDN all manufacturers and countries will be able to develop designs toward a single architecture.

Numerous forces are driving the development of the ISDN. Perhaps the most important in this country is the deregulation of the telephone industry, the emergence of multiple carriers, and a burgeoning demand for high-speed data transmission. Deregulation is occurring at a time when users have multiple options for obtaining information services. One of the primary impediments to exercising these options is a lack of compatibility. Through the ISDN, standard interfaces between the telephone network and other networks such as PBXs, LANs, and interexchange carrier networks and services such as those listed in Table 17.1 are being provided.

The ISDN is not yet a developed concept. Under the auspices of the CCITT, numerous forums have developed the concept that is illustrated in Figure 17.3. In this design the user will be given a 144 kb/s frame, of which 64 kb/s are dedicated to voice, 64 kb/s to data, and 16 kb/s to a data, alarm, and telemetry channel.

For the ISDN to be satisfactory, several technical requirements must be met. The subscriber loop (the connection between the user and the telephone central office) must be fully digital. The central office must be capable of handling both circuit and packet-switched connections, and because the net-

---

TABLE 17.1   Integrated Services Digital Network Typical Services

Videotex
Electronic Mail
Alarm Circuits
Energy Management
Meter Reading
Electronic Information Services
Point of Sale Transaction Services
Facsimile

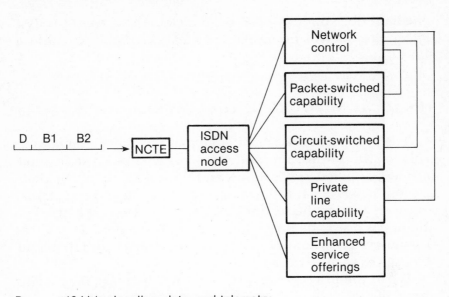

D   16 kb/s signaling, data, and telemetry
B1   64 kb/s voice
B2   64 kb/s data
NCTE   Network channel terminating equipment

FIGURE 17.3   Integrated service digital network architecture

work is fully digital, the customer's telephone set must be capable of digitizing the voice signal.

DIGITAL CONNECTIVITY IN GLOBAL NETWORKS

Although the bulk of data transmission today is over local networks, a substantial amount of data must be transmitted between cities and across the country. Today's long-haul network consists largely of analog facilities deployed over analog broadband microwave radio. Within the last decade digital microwave equipment has become widely available, but it has been used almost exclusively for shorter circuits and has not been applied across the country.

The most promising new technology for long-haul digital transmission is fiber optics. Since competition has been introduced to the long-haul network by the split-up of AT&T, the major carriers have been actively implementing plans for long-haul fiber optics, and it is predictable that coast-to-coast digital circuits will be available at attractive prices within a short time.

THE LOCAL NETWORK OF THE FUTURE

The local network is a vital element in the all-digital network of the future. Presently we conceive of LANs in their business-oriented applications, and that will certainly be their predominate role for the next few years. It is predictable, however, that as the technology matures, demand increases, and prices drop, the LAN will become a household device. Today, nearly every household uses electronic devices that lend themselves to digitization and networking.

When the price is right, demand will increase for a high-speed digital network to control lights and appliances, distribute audio and television entertainment, connect to external networks, monitor and control energy and alarms, access global information banks, and interconnect the multiple computers that every household will eventually have. The list is limited only by human imagination and technology, and it would be a grave error to presume that we have so much as glimpsed the limits.

Appendix A
Data Transmission Recommendations of the CCITT

The X Series of CCITT for data transmission over public data networks.

Number   *Title*

X.1   International user classes of service in public data networks

X.2   International user facilities in public data networks

X.4   General structure of signals of International Alphabet No. 5 code for data transmission over public data networks

X.20   Interface between data terminal equipment and data circuit-terminating equipment for start-stop transmission services on public data networks

X.21   General purpose interface between data terminal equipment and data circuit-terminating equipment for synchronous operation on public data networks

Number	Title
X.24	List of definitions of interchange circuits between data terminal equipment and data circuit-terminating equipment on public data networks
X.25	Interface between data terminal equipment and data circuit-terminating equipment for terminals operating in the packet mode on public data networks
X.26	Electrical characteristics for unbalanced double-current interchange circuits for general use with integrated circuit equipment in the field of data communications
X.27	Electrical characteristics for balanced double-current interchange circuits for general use with integrated circuit equipment in the field of data communications
X.30	Standardization of basic model page-printing machine in accordance with International Alphabet No. 5
X.31	Characteristics for start-stop data terminal equipment using International Alphabet No. 5
X.32	Answer back units for 200 baud start-stop machines in accordance with International Alphabet No. 5
X.33	Standardization of an international text for the measurement of the margin of start-stop machines in accordance with International Alphabet No. 5
X.40	Standardization of frequency-shift modulated transmission systems for the provision of telegraph and data channels by frequency division of a primary group
X.50	Fundamental parameters of a multiplexing scheme for the international interface between synchronous data networks

Number	Title
X.51	Fundamental parameters of a multiplexing scheme for the international interface between synchronous data networks using 10-bit envelope structure
X.60	Common channel signaling for synchronous data applications-data user part
X.70	Terminal and transit control signaling for start-stop services on international circuits between asynchronous data networks
X.71	Decentralized terminal and transit control signaling system on international circuits between synchronous data networks
X.92	Hypothetical reference connections for public synchronous data networks
X.95	Network parameters in public data networks
X.96	Call progress signals in public data networks

The V Series of CCITT for data transmission over the voice circuit or analog networks

V.1	Equivalence between binary notation symbols and the significant conditions of a two-condition code
V.2	Power levels for data transmission over telephone lines
V.3	International Alphabet No. 5 for transmission of data and messages
V.4	General structure of signals of the 7-unit code for data and message transmission
V.10	Use of the telex network for data transmission at the modulation rate of 50 baud
V.11	Automatic calling and/or answering on the telex network

Number	Title
V.13	Answer-back unit simulators
V.15	Use of acoustic couplers for data transmission
V.21	200 baud modem standardized for use in the general switched telephone network
V.22	Standardization of modulation rates and data signaling rates for synchronous data transmission in the general switched telephone network
V.22B	Standardization of modulation rates and data signaling rates on leased telephone circuits
V.23	600/1200 baud modem standardized for use on the general switched telephone networks
V.24	Functions and electrical characteristics of circuits at the interface between data terminal equipment and data circuit-terminating equipment
V.25	Automatic calling and/or answering on the general switched telephone network
V.26	2400 bits/second modem for use on four-wire leased point-to-point circuits
V.26B	2400 bits/second modem for use on the general switched telephone network
V.27	Modem for data signaling rates up to 4800 bits/second over leased circuits
V.28	Electrical characteristics for interface circuits
V.30	Parallel data transmission system for universal use on the general switched telephone network
V.31	Electrical characteristics for contact closure-type interface circuits
V.35	Transmission of 48 kilobits/second data using 60 to 108 kHz group bank circuits

Number	Title
V.40	Error indication with electromechanical equipment
V.41	Code-independent error control system
V.50	Standard limits for transmission quality of data transmission
V.51	Organization of the maintenance of international telephone-type circuits used for data transmission
V.52	Characteristics of distortion and error rate measuring apparatus for data transmission
V.53	Limits for the maintenance of telephone-type circuits used for data transmission
V.56	Comprehensive tests for modems that use their own interface circuits
V.57	Comprehensive test set for high transmission rates

Appendix B

Life Cycle Analysis Methods

In Chapter 16 we discussed the concept of a life cycle evaluation of a product. This appendix provides the basics of how to do one. In a life cycle study, the most difficult part is identifying costs accurately. To simplify this illustration, we'll assume that part is complete.

The steps in a life cycle study are:

1. Identify all costs associated with ownership of the products.
2. Array cash flow in the year in which they occur. Omit all cash flows that are equal for all alternatives.
3. Calculate the net present value of each alternative.
4. Make a tentative choice based on the highest net present value among the alternatives.
5. Test all uncertain values to determine if changing assumptions will alter the outcome of the study.

THE PACIFIC SECURITY COMPANY

The Pacific Security Company has an office force of 50 people, half of whom are equipped with terminals. The data systems department has made a feasibility study of local area networks and has concluded that the purchase of a LAN is economically justified. The terminals must access a central data base that is on a disk file driven by a minicomputer. PSC also needs to share a high-speed printer. They want to install an electronic mail and message system, and they must be able to access a branch office in a distant city over a public data network. They have no requirement for video at the present time, but the company plans the installation of closed-circuit television (CCTV) for security and training within five years.

They have narrowed the choice of LAN to two products which we will call Product A and Product B. Both products have sufficient capacity to handle the network for the next ten years, although Product B will require an additional channel to be activated in five years.

Product A is a baseband system using a CSMA/CD multiple access system. It is fully compatible with the IEEE 802 standard and has sufficient capacity to handle all of PSC's local data communications needs for the next ten years. If this product is chosen, PSC will have to use a separate cable for CCTV. To save on installation costs, it is planned to install both the baseband and the CCTV cable simultaneously, but to defer the addition of amplifiers, splitters, and head end equipment until the television system is installed.

Product B is a broadband system using CSMA/CD and operating at 5 mb/s on one channel of a single cable network. All the network hardware, including splitters, head end equipment, and amplifiers can be used for both CCTV and the data network.

The first step in a life cycle study is to identify all costs associated with ownership of both products. This has been done for both products with the results shown in Table B.1. In a life cycle study it is necessary to evaluate only the factors that are different between products. Any costs that are estimated to be equal, such as transition costs and training in our example, can be omitted without affecting the results of the study. For this reason, a life cycle study does not determine the total cost of implementing a project, but instead the difference in cost of implementing one of two or more alternatives.

A life cycle study should not be confused with a feasibility study. A life cycle study starts with the assumption that an in-

TABLE B.1   Local Area Network Costs

Non-recurring Costs	Product A	Product B
Net. Design and Engr.	9500	16500
Equipment Incl. Shipping	96000	145000
Software Right to Use	10100	14500
Cable	1700	1200
Cable Installation	3200	2500
Equipment Installation	12700	19500
Transition Costs	5000	5000
Additional CCTV Equipment	85000	DNA
Growth Addition	DNA	12000
Training	3500	3500
Total	226700	219700

Recurring Costs (Cost per Year)	Product A	Product B
Downtime Labor Costs	4400	2300
Maintenance	13600	15400
Software Upgrades	1100	
Total	19100	17700

vestment in new equipment is justified. The task in a life cycle study is to determine which equipment is the least costly from the time it is acquired until it is retired from service.

The second step is to array the cash flows by the year in which they occur. A spreadsheet program is a convenient way to display the information and to calculate net present value, which is the third step in the process. In Table B.2 we have included five years of costs after the initial year in which the equipment is purchased. Nonrecurring costs are entered in the year in which they occur. Note that in 1990 Product A has been charged with the cost of the amplifiers and head end equipment needed to add a CCTV system. The growth addition needed with Product B is also shown in 1990.

Recurring expenses such as maintenance are shown in each year. They can either be treated as constant costs, as we have done with software upgrades, or they can be increased each year to reflect your estimates of inflation, as we have done with maintenance and down-time labor costs. In this example, we have inflated the labor related factors by 5 percent per year by instructing the program to multiply each year's expense by 1.05.

Tax effects on cash flow should also be included in the chart, but we have omitted them in this example for the sake of simplicity. Investment tax credit is a positive cash flow that occurs in the year of equipment purchase. It is equally accurate either to deduct ITC from the purchase price or to show it as a separate positive cash flow.

The tax effects of depreciation should also be included as a positive cash flow. If an organization is in the 50 percent incremental income tax bracket, the income tax savings should be half the annual depreciation. All expenses should be shown after taxes. The objective is to model the after-tax cash flow to the enterprise as accurately as possible.

We have also omitted salvage value from the model. Salvage is a positive cash flow at the end of the study period. It can be estimated as a percent of the original investment, or, if you prefer, ignored as having a negligible effect on the outcome of the analysis.

Step three is calculating the net present value of each alternative. We have assumed a cost of money of 14 percent in this example. Because all these entries represent expenditures, the net present value is negative for both products. In using a spreadsheet program for NPV it is easiest to omit the minus signs in the entries as long as there are no positive figures. The product with the highest NPV, in this case Product A, which has the least negative NPV, will extract the least amount of cash from the organization throughout its service life.

If you are using a spreadsheet program to compute NPV, a short explanation of how the process works may be helpful. In Lotus 1, 2, 3, the program used for the computation in Table B.2, the formula for net present value is NPV(.14,C21.G21) + B21. Most other spreadsheets use a similar approach; only the syntax may be somewhat different. This formula causes the program to discount each figure in the total costs row (row 21) from 1986 (column C) through 1990 (column G) to its present value at a 14 percent discount rate. The total for 1985 (column B) is not discounted because it occurs in the year of the study. The program adds the dis-

TABLE B.2   Life Cycle Analysis of Two LANs

Product A Net Present Value

	1985	1986	1987	1988	1989	1990
Network Design and Engr.	9500					
Equipment Costs	96000					
Software Right to Use	10100					
Cable	1700					
Cable Installation	3200					
Equipment Installation	12700					
Additional CCTV Equipment Growth Addition						85000
Downtime Labor Costs	4400	4620	4851	5094	5348	5616
Maintenance	13600	14280	14994	15744	16531	17357
Software Upgrades	1100	1100	1100	1100	1100	1100
Total Costs	152300	20000	20945	21937	22979	109073
Net Present Value, Product A	271022					

Product B Net Present Value

	1985	1986	1987	1988	1989	1990
Network Design and Engr.	16500					
Equipment Costs	145000					
Software Right to Use	14500					
Cable	1200					
Cable Installation	2500					
Equipment Installation	19500					
Additional CCTV Equipment						
Growth Addition						12000
Downtime Labor Costs	2300	2415	2536	2663	2796	2935
Maintenance	15400	16170	16979	17827	18719	19655
Software Upgrades						
Maintenance	13600	14280	14994	15744	16531	17357
Total Costs	216900	32865	34508	36234	38045	51948
Net Present Value, Product B	346244					

counted values to compile the NPV. Table B.3 shows the manual equivalent of the NPV calculation for Product A. There is a slight difference between the manual results and the spreadsheet results because of rounding, but such differences are not significant.

Step four is the process of evaluating your assumptions. Many costs are subject to variation, particularly those costs that will occur in future years. For example, you might want to know the result if Product B could be augmented in 1990 for half the estimated cost. By changing the costs in the spread sheet and rerunning the analysis, you can determine how that would affect the NPV of Product B. You should not conclude solely on the basis of this kind of analysis that Product A is the best one to purchase. As suggested in Chapters 15 and 16, there is a great deal more to consider than cost. However, you should be aware that on the basis of this analysis, Product B will cost the enterprise more money. Whether it is worth it or not is a matter for management to decide.

As you can see from this example, the life cycle study process is not complicated. As we mentioned at the start of this appendix, the difficult part of the analysis is determining what cost factors to use. To obtain the most accurate results, it is important to select study factors such as the cost of money and length of study with care. Also, your assumptions about the inflation of recurring costs will have an important effect on the outcome. With a spreadsheet program any uncertainties can be accommodated by changing the assumptions and rerun-

TABLE B.3 Net Present Value Calculation

Year	Cash Flow	Present Value Factor at 14 percent	Present Value
1985	152,300	1.0000	152,300
1986	20,000	.8772	17,544
1987	20,945	.7695	16,117
1988	21,937	.6750	14,807
1989	22,979	.5921	13,606
1990	109,073	.5194	56,653
		Net present value	271,027

ning the analysis to determine if any of the changes alter the conclusions.

For more details on how to conduct a life cycle study, we referred to the author's book *Automating Your Office: How To Do It, How To Justify It* (McGraw-Hill, 1984).

Appendix C
Local Area Network Product Features and Suppliers

This appendix contains the names and addresses of the principle LAN suppliers and the name of their LAN products. PBXs and data switches are not included in this summary. The manufacturers or their distributors can be contacted for further information.

Manufacturer	*Product*
A. B. Dick Co. 5700 West Touhy Ave. Chicago, IL 60648 312-763-1900	The Loop
Altos Computer Systems 2360 Bering Dr. San Jose, CA 95131 408-946-6700	Altos Net
Apollo Computer Inc. 15 Elizabeth Dr. Chelmsford, MA 01824 617-256-6600	DOMAIN

Manufacturer	*Product*
Apple Computer Inc. 20525 Mariani Ave. Cupertino, CA 95014 408-973-3019	AppleNet
AT&T Teletype Corp. 5555 Touhy Ave. Skokie, IL 60077 312-982-2000	Teletype 4540 Local Connect
Braegan Corp. 525 Los Coches St. Milpitas, CA 95035 408-945-1900	ELAN
Complexx Systems, Inc. P. O. Box 12597 Huntsville, AL 35802 205-882-0207	XLAN
Compucorp 1901 S Bundy Dr. Los Angeles, CA 90025 213-820-2503	OmegaNet
Computer Network Corp. 4030 N. 27th Ave. Phoenix, AZ 85017 602-274-3233	Data Loop Exchange 10 Data Loop Exchange 320
Concord Data Systems 303 Bear Hill Rd. Waltham, MA 02154 617-890-1394	Token/Net
Contel Information Systems, Inc. 130 Steamboat Road Great Neck, NY 11024 516-829-5900	ConTelNet

Manufacturer	*Product*
Convergent Technologies 1500 Augustine Dr. Santa Clara, CA 95051 408-727-8830	Local Resource Sharing Network
Corvus Systems Inc. 2029 O'Toole Ave. San Jose, CA 95131 408-946-7700	Omninet
Cromemco Inc. 280 Bernardo Ave. Mountain View, CA 94043 415-964-7400	C-Net
Data General Corp. 4400 Computer Dr. Westboro, MA 01581 617-366-8911	XODIAC Network Bus Local- Area Network
Datapoint Corp. 9725 Datapoint Dr. San Antonio, TX 78284 512-699-7059	ARCNET
Destek Group 830C Evelyn Ave. Sunnyvale, CA 94086 408-737-7211	DESNET
Digilog Business Systems, Inc. Welsh Rd. & Park Dr. P. O. Box 355 Montgomeryville, PA 18936 215-628-4810	System 1800
Digital Equipment Corp. 129 Parker St. Maynard, MA 01754 617-493-4097	DECdataway Ethernet

Manufacturer   *Product*

Digital Microsystems Inc.   HiNet
1755 Embarcadero
Oakland, CA 94606
415-532-3686

Gandalf Data, Inc.   PACXNET
1019 S Noel Ave.
Wheeling, IL 60090
312-541-6060

Gould, Inc.   MODBUS
1280 E. Big Beaver Rd.
Troy, MI 48084   MODWAY
313-524-2700

Hewlett-Packard   Interface Bus
1501 Page Mill Rd.
Palo Alto, CA 94304
415-851-1501

InteCom, Inc.   LANmark
601 Intecom Dr.
Allen, TX 75002
214-727-9141

Interactive Systems/3M   VIDEODATA
3920 Varsity Dr.   LAN/1
Ann Arbor, MI 48104
313-973-1500

International Business Machines   8100 Loop
Information Systems Group
1133 Westchester Ave.   Series 1 Ring
White Plains, NY 10604
914-696-1900

Interlan Inc.   NET/PLUS
3 Lyberty Way
Westford, MA 01886
617-692-3900

Manufacturer	*Product*
Intersil Systems, Inc. 1275 Hammerwood Ave. Sunnyvale, CA 94086 408-743-4300	GEnet
Intertec Data Systems 2300 Broad River Rd. Columbia, SC 29210 803-798-9100	CompuStar
Logica Inc. 666 Third Ave. New York, NY 10017 212-599-0828	Polynet
Orchid Technology 47790 Westinghouse Dr. Fremont, CA 94539 415-490-8586	PCnet
M/A-COM DCC, Inc. 11717 Exploration Lane Germantown, MD 20874 301-428-5500	Infobus
M/A-COM Linkabit, Inc. 3033 Science Park Rd. San Diego, CA 92121 714-457-2340	IDX-3000 Local Communication Network
NCR Corporation 1700 Patterson Blvd. Dayton, OH 45479 513-449-2000	NCR Decision Net
Nestar Systems, Inc. 2582 E. Bayshore Rd. Palo Alto, CA 94303 415-493-2223	Cluster/One Plan 1000 Plan 4000

Manufacturer	*Product*
Network Systems Corp. 7600 Boone Ave. North Brooklyn Park Minneapolis, MN 55428 612-425-2202	HYPERchannel
North Star Computers, Inc. 14440 Catalina St. San Leandro, CA 94577 415-357-8500	NorthNet
Novell Data Systems 1170 N. Industrial Park Dr. Orem, UT 84057 801-226-8202	ShareNet X ShareNet S
Ohio Scientific Inc. 7 Oak Park Bedford, MA 01730 617-275-3030	IBS-NET
Orange Compuco, Inc. 17801-G S.E. Main Irvine, CA 92714 714-957-8075	ULCnet
Prolink Corp. 5757 Central Ave. Boulder, CO 80301 303-477-2800	Proloop
Proteon Associates, Inc. 24 Crescent St. Waltham, MA 02154 617-894-1980	ProNET
Racal-Milgo 8600 N.W. 41st St. P. O. Box 520399 Miami, FL 33152 305-592-8600	PLANET

Manufacturer	*Product*
Scientific Data Systems 344 Main St. Venice, CA 90291 213-390-8673	SDSNET
Siecor Corp. P. O. Box 12726 Research Triangle Park, NC 27709 919-544-3791	FiberLAN
Sperry P. O. Box 500 Blue Bell, PA 19424 215-542-4011	SHINPADS SPERRYLINK
Standard Engineering Corp. 44800 Industrial Dr. Fremont, CA 94538 415-657-7555	Microlink
Starnet Data Systems 1331 W. Evans Ave. Denver, CO 80223 303-935-3566	Starnet II
Stratus Computer, Inc. 17 Strathmore Rd. Natick, MA 01760 617-653-1466	StratLINK
Syntech International, Inc. P. O. Box 28810 Dallas, TX 75228 214-340-0379	MARS/NET
Syntrex, Inc. 246 Industrial Way West Eatontown, NJ 07724 201-542-1500	SYNNet

Manufacturer   *Product*

Sytek, Inc.   LocalNet 20
1225 Charleston Rd.
Mountain View, CA 94043   LocalNet 40
415-966-7300

Tecmar Inc.   Elan
6225 Cochran Rd.
Solon, OH 44139
216-349-0600

Teltone Corp   DCS-2 Data
10801 120th N.E.   Carrier System
P. O. Box 657
Kirkland, WA 98033
206-827-9626

Three Rivers Computer Corp.   Ethernet
720 Gross St.
Pittsburgh, PA 15224
412-621-6250

3COM Corp.   Etherlink
1390 Shorbird Way
Mountain View, CA 94043
415-961-9602

Ungerman Bass, Inc.   Net/One
2560 Mission College Blvd.
Santa Clara, CA 95050
408-496-0111

Valmet Inc.   Millway
7 Westchester Plaza
Elmsford, NY 10523
914-347-4440

Vector Graphic, Inc.   LINC
500 North Ventu Park Rd.
Thousand Oaks, CA 91320
805-499-5831

Manufacturer	Product
Wang Laboratories, Inc. One Industrial Ave. Lowell, MA 01851 617-459-5000	Wangnet
Xerox Corp 1341 W. Mockingbird Lane Dallas, TX 75247 214-536-9129	Ethernet
Zilog, Inc. 1315 Dell Ave. Campbell, CA 95008 408-370-8000	UNET
Ztel, Inc. York St. Andover Industrial Park Andover, MA 01810 617-470-2900	AXIS

TABLE C.1 Local area networks outline

COMPANY	NETWORK	NETWORK TYPE		ACCESS METHOD			TRANSMISSION SPEED				CABLE LENGTH			GATEWAYS				APPLICATION AREA				
		Baseband	Broadband	Contention	Token passing	Other	to 1M bps	to 2M bps	to 10M bps	over 10M bps	to 2000 ft	to 5000 ft	over 5000 ft	IBM SNA/SDLC	X.25	Xerox Ethernet	Other	General Business	Electronic Mail	Word Processing	Industrial	Other
A.B. Dick	The Loop	●		●			●						●	●			●	●	●			●
Alspa Computer Inc	ALSPA-NET	●		●									●					●				●
Altos Computer Sys	WorkNet	●		●			●						●					●				
AT&T Teletype	Teletype 4540 LC						●						●	●				●				
Amtel Systems	Messenger	●					●						●					●				●
Apollo Computer	DOMAIN	●		●						●			●				●	●	●	●		●
Applitek Corp	UniLAN		●		●					●			●					●				●
AST Research	PCnet	●		●			●						●					●				
AST Research	PCnet II	●		●				●					●					●				
Braegen Corp	ELAN		●							●			●					●				
Bridge Comm Inc	Ethernet	●		●					●				●			●	●	●	●			●
Codenoll Tech	Ethernet	●		●					●				●			●		●				●
Codex Corp	Net/One	●	●	●					●				●			●	●	●	●			●
Complexx Sys. Inc.	XLAN		●				●						●					●				
Compucorp	OmegaNet	●			●		●						●					●	●			
Computer Network	DLX-10	●		●			●				●						●	●	●	●		●
Computer Network	DLX-320	●		●					●		●						●	●	●	●		●
Concord Data Systems	Token/Net	●	●		●					●			●					●				●
Contel Info Sys	ConTelNet	●		●					●				●					●	●			●
Contel Info Sys	STAR-Eleven	●		●					●				●					●	●			●
Convergent Systems	Local Resource Shar	●		●					●				●	●				●				●
Corvus	Omninet	●				●	●						●	●			●	●	●	●		●
Cromemco	C-Net	●				●	●						●					●				●
Data General	XODIAC Network Bus	●		●					●				●	●		●	●	●	●	●		●
Datapoint	ARCnet	●			●			●					●	●			●	●	●	●		●

255

TABLE C.1 (continued)

COMPANY	NETWORK	Baseband	Broadband	Contention	Token passing	Other	to 1M bps	to 2M bps	to 10M bps	over 10M bps	to 2000 ft	to 5000 ft	over 5000 ft	IBM SNA/SDLC	X.25	Xerox Ethernet	Other	General Business	Electronic Mail	Word Processing	Industrial	Other
		NETWORK TYPE		ACCESS METHOD			TRANSMISSION SPEED				CABLE LENGTH			GATEWAYS				APPLICATION AREA				
Davong Systems Inc	MultiLink	•		•			•				•			•	•			•		•		•
DBS International	DBS-NET	•			•		•				•			•	•			•	•			•
DESTEK Group	DESNET	•	•			•			•			•				•		•				•
Develcon Elct Inc.	Develnet		•		•		•						•						•			
Digital Equipment	DECdataway	•			•		•				•			•				•	•		•	
Digital Equipment	Ethernet	•		•					•				•	•	•	•		•	•	•		•
Digital Microsystems	HiNet	•			•		•				•						•	•		•		
Doeltz Network Inc	Doeltz Network	•		•				•				•		•	•			•	•			•
Gandalf Data	PACXNET	•				•	•						•	•	•			•				•
Gateway Comm. Inc.	G/Net	•		•					•			•		•		•		•	•	•		•
General Electric	GEnet	•			•			•					•	•	•			•	•		•	•
Gould	MODBUS	•			•		•				•			•							•	
Gould	MODWAY	•			•			•					•	•							•	
Hewlett-Packard	Interface Bus	•		•					•		•			•				•				•
Hewlett-Packard	LAN 9000	•			•				•				•	•		•		•	•	•		•
Hewlett-Packard	SRM	•		•					•			•		•		•		•	•	•		•
Honeywell	TDC 3000	•			•			•				•		•				•			•	
Iconix Corp	Cinchnet	•		•					•				•	•		•		•	•	•		•
Inforex, Inc.	ULTRANET	•			•		•					•		•				•	•			•
Intecom	LANmark	•			•				•				•	•	•			•	•	•		•
Interactive Sys/3M	VIDEODATA		•	•					•				•			•		•				•
Interactive Sys/3M	LAN/1	•		•					•				•			•		•	•	•		•
Interlan	NET/PLUS	•		•					•				•	•	•	•		•	•	•		•
Int'l Bus Mach (IBM)	8100 Loop	•			•		•						•	•				•				•
Int'l Bus Mach (IBM)	Series/1 Ring	•			•			•					•	•	•			•	•	•		•

256

Company	Product
Int'l Bus Mach (IBM)	PC Cluster
Intertec Data Systems	CompuStar
Lanier	LBS 5000
Logica	Polynet
M/A-COM DCC	Infobus
M/A-COM Linkabit	IDX-3000
Micom Systems	INSTANET
Molecular Company	SuperMicro Multiuser
Morrow	MORROW NETWORK
NBI, Inc	NBINET
NCR Corp	Decision Net
NCR Corp	MIRLAN
Nestar Systems	PLAN 4000 Series
Network Systems	HYPERchannel
Network Systems	HYPERbus
North Star Computer	North Net
Novell Data Systems	ShareNet
Orange Compuco	ULCnet
Orchid Technology	PCnet/PCnet Plus
Percom Data Corp	PerComNet
Perq Systems	Ethernet
Pragmatronics	TIENET
Prime Computer	RINGNET
Prolink	Proloop
Proteon	proNET
Racal-Milgo	PLANET
Santa Clara Systems	PCnet
Scientific Data	SDSNET
Sidereal Corp	MIC-LINK
Sperry	SHINPADS
Starnet Data Systems	Starnet II
Stratus Computer	StrataLINK
Syntech	MARS/NET
Syntrex	SYNNet
Sytek	LocalNet20

TABLE C.1 (continued)

COMPANY	NETWORK	NETWORK TYPE		ACCESS METHOD			TRANSMISSION SPEED				CABLE LENGTH			GATEWAYS				APPLICATION AREA				
		Baseband	Broadband	Contention	Token passing	Other	to 1M bps	to 2M bps	to 10M bps	over 10M bps	to 2000 ft	to 5000 ft	over 5000 ft	X.25	IBM SNA/SDLC	Xerox Ethernet	Other	General Business	Electronic Mail	Word Processing	Industrial	Other
Sytek	LocalNet40	•	—	•	—	—	—	—	•	—	—	—	•	—	—	—	—	•	—	—	•	•
Tandy Corp	ARCnet	—	—	—	•	—	—	—	•	—	—	•	—	—	—	—	—	•	—	—	—	•
Teltone	DCS-2/2S Data Carrier	—	•	—	—	•	—	•	—	—	—	•	—	—	—	—	—	•	•	•	—	•
3COM	Ethernet/UNET	•	—	•	—	—	—	—	•	—	•	—	—	—	—	•	—	—	•	•	—	•
3COM	Etherlink	•	—	•	—	—	—	—	•	—	•	—	—	—	—	•	—	—	•	•	—	•
Ungermann-Bass	Net/One Baseband	•	—	•	—	—	—	—	•	—	—	—	•	—	—	—	—	•	•	•	•	•
Ungermann-Bass	Net/One Broadband	—	•	•	—	—	—	—	•	—	—	—	•	—	—	—	—	•	•	•	•	•
Ungermann-Bass	Fiber Optic Net/One	•	—	•	—	—	—	—	•	—	—	—	•	—	—	—	—	•	•	•	•	•
Ungermann-Bass	Net/One Thin Coax	•	—	•	—	—	—	—	•	—	—	—	•	—	—	—	—	•	•	•	•	•
Valmet	Millway	•	—	—	—	—	•	—	—	—	—	—	—	—	—	—	—	—	—	—	—	—
Vector Graphics	LINC	•	—	•	—	—	—	—	•	—	•	—	—	—	—	—	—	•	—	—	—	•
Wang Laboratories	Wangnet	—	•	—	—	•	—	—	•	—	—	—	•	—	—	—	—	•	•	•	—	•
Xerox	Ethernet	—	—	•	—	—	—	—	•	—	—	—	•	—	—	—	—	•	—	—	—	•
Xyplex, Inc	XYPLEX System	—	•	—	—	—	—	—	•	—	—	—	•	—	—	—	—	•	—	—	—	•
Zilog	UNET	•	—	—	—	—	—	—	•	—	—	•	—	—	—	—	—	•	—	—	—	•
Ztel	AXIS	•	—	—	—	—	—	—	•	—	—	—	•	—	—	—	—	•	—	—	—	•

SOURCE: This information is taken from *Communications Systems*, a monthly updated information service available from *Data Decisions*, 20 Brace Road, Cherry Hill, N.J. (609) 429-7100.

Glossary

Access The capability of terminals to be interconnected for the purpose of exchanging traffic.

American National Standards Institute (ANSI) The U.S. agency responsible for coordinating the development of all standards.

American Standard Code for Information Interexchange (ASCII) A 7-bit (plus one parity bit) coding system used for encoding characters for transmission over a data network.

Analog A transmission mode that transmits information by converting it to a variable electrical signal.

Asynchronous Data transmissions over a network with each character containing a start and a stop bit in order to synchronize operations between transmitting and receiving terminals.

Attempts The number of times a terminal accesses or attempts to access a network or switching system.

Backoff Algorithm The formula developed for a contention network that allows the media access controller to determine when to reattempt to access the network after collision.

Bandwidth The range of frequencies a communications channel can support without excessive attenuation.

Baseband A form of modulation in which data signals are pulsed directly onto the transmission medium without frequency division.

Binary A numbering system consisting of the two digits, zero and one.

Bit The smallest single unit of information that can be processed or transported over a network. Contraction of the words BInary digiT.

Blockage   The state of a network when it is incapable of passing information because the load offered exceeds the network capacity. In a blocked condition, the load offered to the network is delayed until the blockage is cleared.

Branching Tree   A network topology in which nodes or terminals are connected to multiple branches that are bridged together with impedance-matching circuitry.

Bridge   Circuitry used to interconnect networks with a common set of higher level protocols.

Broadband   A form of modulation that forms multiple channels by dividing the transmission medium into discrete frequency segments.

Bus   A network topology bridging terminals across the transmission medium on a multi-drop basis.

Byte   A set of eight bits of information equivalent to a character. Also called octet.

Carrier   A system of multiplexing for supporting multiple channels on a transmission medium.

Carrier Sense Multiple Access with Collision Detection (CSMA/CD)   A system used in contention networks where the network interface unit listens for the presence of a carrier before attempting to send and detects the presence of a collision by monitoring for a distorted pulse.

Central Processing Unit (CPU)   The control logic used to execute instructions in a computer.

Channel Bank   A device used to multiplex multiple analog or digital channels together for transmission over a communications medium.

Circuit   A transmission path between nodes on a network. A circuit can be either a physical (wired) connection or a virtual connection through which nodes share the transmission path with other users.

Circuit Switching   A method of network access that connects terminals by switching together the circuits to which they are attached. In a circuit switched network the terminals have full real-time access to each other up to the bandwidth of the circuit.

Coaxial Cable A cable consisting of a single conductor surrounded by an insulating spacer and a metallic shield.

Collision A condition that occurs when two or more terminals on a contention network attempt to acquire access to the network simultaneously.

Community Antenna Television (CATV) An analog network used for transporting multiple 6 MHz channels for video, data, or voice signals.

Computerized Branch Exchange (CBX) A form of PBX using a computer for central control, usually with a nonblocking network and integrated voice and data capability.

Consultative Committee for International Telephone and Telegraph (CCITT) A division of the International Telecommunications Union devoted to establishing international telecommunications standards.

Contention A form of multiple access to a network that allocates capacity on a first-come-first-served basis.

Cyclical Redundancy Checking (CRC) A data error detecting system that subjects an information block to a mathematical process designed to ensure that errors cannot occur undetected.

Data Circuit-terminating Equipment (DCE) Equipment designed to establish a connection to a network, condition the input and output of DTE for transmission over the network, and terminate a completed connection.

Data Terminal Equipment (DTE) Any form of computer, peripheral, or terminal that can be used for originating or receiving data over a communication channel.

Datagram A single information packet that is sent over a network as an individual unit without regard to previous or subsequent packets.

Diameter The distance between the outermost nodes on a network.

Digital A mode of transmitting information coded in binary form.

Echo A portion of a transmitted signal reflected back to the sender.

Electronic Industries Association (EIA) An association

of electronic equipment manufacturers that has developed data communications standards such as the RS 232-C for interconnecting DCE and DTE.

Error Any discrepancy between a transmitted and a received data signal.

Ethernet A proprietary contention bus network developed by Xerox, Digital Equipment Corporation, and Intel, that formed the basis for the IEEE 802.3 standard.

Expanded Binary Coded Decimal Interexchange Code (EBCDIC) An 8-bit coding scheme used for encoding characters for transmission over a data network.

Fiber Optics A transmission system consisting of thin, glass fiber capable of conducting light pulses, a light source, and a light detector. A fiber optic system is capable of transporting high-speed data by rapid on/off pulses of light.

Frequency Division Multiplexing A method of imposing multiple channels on a transmission medium by assigning each channel to a separate frequency.

Full-Duplex A data communication circuit that supports data transmissions in both directions simultaneously.

Gateway Circuitry that interconnects networks through protocol conversion.

Global Network A communications network that offers world-wide access.

Half-duplex A data communications circuit that supports data transmissions one direction at a time.

Head End The equipment used in a broadband network to split the transmitting and receiving frequencies or to connect the transmitting cable to the receiving cable.

Holding Time The amount of time a terminal retains a connection to a network or switching system.

Institute of Electrical and Electronics Engineers (IEEE) An association of engineering societies, including the Computer Society, that developed the 802 standards for local area networks.

Impedance The characteristic of a network describing its opposition to the flow of alternating current.

International Standards Organization (ISO) An association of the standards organizations of the member nations.

International Telecommunications Union (ITU) An organization established under the United Nations to form international standards for telecommunications and radio.

Life Cycle Analysis The process of estimating the total cost of product ownership by determining the present worth of all cash flows discounted at the organization's cost of money.

Local Network A data communications network that supports multiple access for data communications over a narrow range, usually within a building and over a distance of one mile or less.

Local Area Network (LAN) A form of local network using one of the nonswitched multiple access technologies.

Long Haul Network See Global Network.

Longitudinal Redundancy Checking (LRC) A data error checking system in which data are sent in blocks with a final parity check character at the end of each block.

Loss The reduction in signal level from a transmitting terminal to a receiving terminal over a circuit.

Mean Time Between Failures (MTBF) The average time a device or system operates without failing.

Mean Time to Repair (MTTR) The average time required for a qualified technician to repair a failed device or system.

Media Access Controller (MAC) The control circuitry in a LAN that converts the protocols of the DTE to those required by the LAN.

Media Access Unit (MAU) A device used in local area networks to enable DTE to access the transmission medium.

Message Switching A form of network access where a message is forwarded from a terminal to a central switch that stores it and after some delay forwards it to the addressee.

Metropolitan Network A communications network that extends over a metropolitan area and usually provides access to multiple organizations.

Modem A modem is used to convert analog signals to digital form and vice versa. A contraction of the term MOdulator/DEModulator.

Multi-drop A circuit dedicated to communications between multiple terminals connected to the same circuit.

Multiple Access The capability of multiple terminals connected to the same network to access one another by means of a common addressing scheme and protocol.

Multiplexer A device used for combining several lower-speed channels into a higher-speed channel.

Net Present Value The sum of all discounted cash flows over the lifetime of an investment minus the original investment capital.

Network Diameter The distance between the outermost terminals on a network.

Network Interface Unit A collective term describing all the circuitry needed to interface a terminal to a network.

Node A major point at which terminals are given access to a network.

Noise Any unwanted interfering signal that appears on a circuit.

Octet A group of eight bits. Also known as a *byte.*

Open System Interconnection (OSI) A model developed by the CCITT for standardizing data transmission functions so equipment made by different manufacturers can be interconnected.

Overhead Any noninformation bits such as headers, error checking bits, start and stop bits used for controlling a network.

Packet A unit of data information consisting of header, information, error detection, and trailer records.

Packet Assembler/Disassembler (PAD) A device used on a packet-switched network to assemble information into packets and to convert received packets into a continuous data stream.

Packet Switching A method of allocating network time by forming data into packets and relaying them to the destination under control of processors at each major node. The network determines packet routing during its transport.

Parallel   A transmission path in which data bits travel over eight separate conductors simultaneously.

Parity   A bit or series of bits appended to a character or block of characters to ensure that either an odd or even number of bits are transmitted. Parity is used for error detection.

Permanent Virtual Circuit (PVC)   Circuit routing that is defined through a network between two or more terminals.

Point-to-Point   A circuit dedicated to communication between two terminals.

Polling   A method of extracting data from remote terminals to a host. The host accesses the terminal, determines if it has traffic to send, and causes traffic to be uploaded to the host.

Port   An access point in a computer or switching system where the system is capable of exchanging data with external devices.

Protocol   The conventions used in a network for establishing communications compatibility between terminals, and for maintaining the line discipline while they are connected to the network.

Private Branch Exchange (PBX) also referred to as *Private Automatic Branch Exchange*   A circuit-switching system designed for the private use of one or more organizations and capable of handling both voice and data traffic between terminals to metropolitan and global networks.

Pulse Code Modulation (PCM)   A method of converting analog signals to digital and vice versa by sampling the analog signal and converting each sample to a digital byte at the sending end and reversing the process at the receiving end.

Regenerator   A digital repeater used to eliminate the effects of pulse distortion in a digital network.

Repeater   An electronic device used to amplify an analog signal or regenerate a digital signal.

Request For Quotations (RFQ)   A request from a prospective purchaser to suppliers in order to obtain product pricing and technical information.

Response Time   The time interval between the last character input to a network and the last character output to the host.

Ring   A network topology in which each node is inserted into a network that is deployed in a circular configuration.

Split-channel Modem   A modem that uses separate audio frequency tones for sending and receiving to enable full duplex data transmission over a two-wire circuit.

Splitter   A device designed for connecting coaxial cable branches together on a broadband network without disrupting the impedance of the network.

Star   A network topology in which each node is connected at a central point.

Statistical Multiplexing   A form of data multiplexing in which the time on a communications channel is assigned to terminals only when they have data to transport.

Store and Forward   A method of switching messages in which a message or packet is sent from the originating terminal to a central unit where it is held for retransmission to the receiving terminal.

Switched Virtual Circuit (SVC)   Circuit routing that is established through a network with each packet transmittal.

Synchronous   A method of transmitting data over a network wherein the sending and receiving terminals are synchronized by a clock signal embedded in the data.

Tap   The physical point of connection between a media access unit and the transmission medium.

Terminal   A collective term referring to any DTE that can be connected to a network node that is capable of sending and receiving data.

Termination   A device used in baseband networks to terminate the transmission medium in its characteristic impedance to avoid impedance irregularities.

Throughput   The effective rate of transmission of information between two points excluding noninformation (overhead) bits.

Time Compression Multiplexing (TCM)   A method of sending full duplex data over a two-wire circuit by sending data at twice the effective speed and rapidly reversing the direction of transmission.

Time Domain Reflectometer (TDR)   A device used to detect irregularities in cable by sending a pulse on the cable and determining the time for a pulse to be reflected from the irregularity back to the source.

Time Division Multiplexing A method of combining several communication channels by dividing a channel into time increments and assigning each channel to a time slot. Multiple channels are interleaved when each channel is assigned the entire bandwidth of the backbone channel for a short period of time.

Token A software mark or packet that circulates among network nodes.

Token Passing A method of allocating network access wherein a terminal can send traffic only after it has acquired the network's token.

Topology The architecture of a network, or the way circuits are connected to link the network nodes together.

Transceiver A device used in contention networks for sending data over the network and receiving data from the network.

Trunk A specialized circuit used to connect circuit switches to one another.

Twinaxial Cable A cable consisting of two center conductors surrounded by an insulating spacer and a metallic shield.

Value Added Network A network in which some form of processing of a data signal takes place, or information is added to the signal by the network.

Vertical Redundancy Checking (VRC) A data error checking system that detects transmission errors by adding an extra parity bit to each transmitted character.

Virtual Circuit A circuit that is established between two terminals by assigning a logical path over which data can flow. A virtual circuit can either be permanent, in which terminals are assigned a permanent path or switched, in which the circuit is reestablished each time a terminal has data to send.

Bibliography

Abramson, Paul and Noel, Franc E. "Matching the Media to Local Network Requirements." *Data Communications* 12 (July 1983): 115–123.

Cooper, Edward B., and Edholm, Philip K. "Design Issues in Broadband Local Networks." *Data Communications* 12 (February 1983): 109–122.

Chorafas, Dimitris N. *Designing and Implementing Local Area Networks.* New York: McGraw-Hill, Inc., 1984.

Cunningham, D. Jay. "The Impact of Fiber Optics on Local Area Networks." *Telephony* 204 (January 3, 1983): 28–33.

Davis, George R. *The Local Network Handbook.* New York: McGraw-Hill, Inc., 1982.

Derfler, Frank, Jr., and Stallings, William. *A Manager's Guide to Local Networks.* Englewood Cliffs, N.J.: Prentice-Hall, 1983.

Dhawan, Ashok. "One Way to End the Brouhaha Over Choosing an Optimal LAN." *Data Communications* 13 (March 1984): 287–296.

Frank, Howard. "Broadband Versus Baseband Local Area Networks." *Telecommunications* 17 (March 1983): 35–38.

Fredricksson, Staffan. "Shopping Optics: A Comparative Guide to Coaxial Versus Fiber Technologies." *Data Communications* 13 (March 1984): 205–213.

Freeman, Roger L. *Telecommunications System Engineering.* New York: John Wiley & Sons, 1980.

Fridman, Jonathan D. "Laser Communications in Information Systems." *Telecommunications* 17 (September 1983): 94–128.

Gee, K. C. E. *Local Area Networks.* Manchester, England: The National Computing Centre, Ltd. 1982.

Graube, Maris. "Local Area Nets: A Pair of Standards." *IEEE Spectrum* 23 (June 1982): 60–64.

Green, James H. *Automating Your Office: How To Do It, How To Justify It.* New York: McGraw-Hill, Inc., 1984.

Grellner, Richard J. "Developing a Gateway to the Information Age." *Telephone* 205 (December 12, 1983): 66–72.

Hanson, Del. "Application of Fiber Optics to Local Area Networks." *Telecommunications* 16 (December 1982): 33–38.

Institute of Electrical and Electronic Engineers, Inc. *IEEE Project 802 Local Area Network Standards* Los Alamitus, Calif. *Draft IEEE Standard 802.2 Logical Link Control,* Draft D, November 1982.

———. *Draft IEEE Standard 802.3 CSMA/CD Access Method and Physical Layer Specifications.* Revision D, December 1982.

———. *Draft IEEE Standard 802.4 Token-Passing Bus Access Method and Physical Layer Specifications.* Draft D, December, 1982.

———. *Draft IEEE Standard 802.5 Token Ring Access Method and Physical Layer Specifications.* Working draft, December 1983.

Johnson, L. Marvin. *Quality Assurance Program Evaluation.* Santa Fe Springs, Calif.: Stockton Trade Press, Inc., 1970.

Kepner, Charles H., and Tregoe, Benjamin B. *The Rational Manager.* Princeton, N.J.: Kepner-Tregoe, Inc., 1965.

Machrone, Bill. "Battle of the Network Stars." *PC Magazine* 2 (November 1983): 92–103.

Martin, James. *Computer Networks and Distributed Processing.* Englewood Cliffs, N.J.: Prentice-Hall, 1981.

Mier, Edwin E. "Packet Switching and X.25—Where to From Here?" *Data Communications* 12 (October 1983): 121–138.

Naisbitt, John *Megatrends.* New York: Warner Books, 1982.

Pfister, George M., and O'Brien, Bradley V. "Comparing the CBX to the Local Network—And The Winner Is?" *Data Communications* 11 (July 1982): 103–113.

Pfister, George M. "A Practical Look at Integration Schemes for Voice and Data on PBX Systems." 11 *Telephony* 202 (March 1, 1982): 38–44.

Raffensperger, Ronald. "The Broadband Switch: A Powerful Bid for Control of the Automated Office." 206 *Telephony* (March 12, 1984): 32–41.

Rosenberger, William F. "WangNet in the Office." *Telephone Engineer and Management* 86 (January 1, 1983): 54–59.

Sherman, Kenneth. *Data Communications: A Users Guide.* Reston, Virginia: Reston Publishing Co., Inc., 1981.

Rutkowsky, A. M. "The International Telecommunications Union and the United States." *Telecommunications* 17 (October 1983): 35–42.

Scott, Thomas J. "How to Avoid Some Common Pitfalls of a Local Net Installation." *Data Communications* 13 (March 1984): 243–256.

Stallings, William. *Local Networks: An Introduction.* New York: Macmillan Publishing Co., 1984.

Tofler, Alvin. *The Third Wave.* New York: William Morrow, 1980.

Tannenbaum, Andrew S. *Computer Networks.* Englewood Cliffs, N.J.: Prentice-Hall, 1981.

Woodward, D. P. "Digital Crosstalk on Twisted Pair Telephone Premise Wiring." *Telephony* 206 (March 12, 1984): 76–92.

Index

continued

continued